VANCE PACKARD

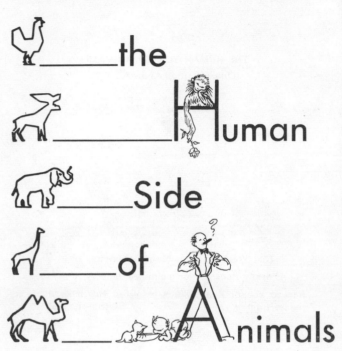

the Human Side of

(Original title: ANIMAL IQ)

Illustrated with 42 photographs by
Lilo Hess from Three Lions, Inc.

 POCKET BOOKS, INC. • NEW YORK

THE HUMAN SIDE OF ANIMALS
(Original title: ANIMAL IQ)

Dial Press edition published February, 1950

Pocket Book edition published January, 1951

Revised Pocket Book edition published November, 1961
1st printing.................................September, 1961

This Pocket Book is compiled from the previous editions
and contains new material. It is printed from brand-new
plates made from completely reset, clear, easy-to-read type.

•

Pocket Book editions are distributed in the U.S. by Affili-
ated Publishers, Inc., 630 Fifth Avenue, New York 20, N.Y.

•

Notice: Pocket Book editions are published by Pocket Books,
Inc. Trademark registered in the United States and other countries.

Now in his middle forties, Vance Packard is an author who has written many books and articles drawn from studies in the field of social science. A number of his articles on animal behavior have appeared in national magazines.

Born in Granville Summit, Pennsylvania, Mr. Packard attended Penn State and Columbia University and has lectured on writing at Columbia and New York University. Mr. Packard now lives in New Canaan, Connecticut, with his family.

THE HUMAN SIDE OF ANIMALS, Vance Packard's first POCKET BOOK edition, was originally published by The Dial Press, Inc., as ANIMAL IQ.

Other books by Vance Packard

The Hidden Persuaders

†*The Status Seekers*

The Waste Makers

*Published in a CARDINAL edition.

†To be published in a GIANT CARDINAL edition.

CONTENTS

Introduction · To Some Sourpusses and Showoffs

MAN, in his conceit, likes to think that when brains and personality were passed out, he was given the monopoly on both for this particular planet.

He invented the expression "dumb animals" and applies it freely to all other possible claimants. Man did this to make it completely clear to any skeptics that all members of the animal kingdom—except possibly his "best friends," the dog, horse and cat—are stupid clods in a nether world of semiconsciousness.

In recent years more than a hundred psychologists have become curious to know the real facts about animal mentality and personality. They have devised all sorts of ingenious tests and strategies to get inside the worlds of different animals.

Can some animals really think, and feel emotions? If so, which are the brainiest?

Some of the findings of the psychologists have been startling. It is true that certain animals are numskulls, Grade A morons. But on the other hand several psychologists have found themselves being outwitted by chimpanzees on their own tests! And one psychologist who pitted a group of college students against a group of white rats on a maze test was astonished to find that the students came out a poor second.

Also, the psychologists have found that some animals possess personalities as vivid—and sometimes as objectionable—as any we find in the human species. Certain animals, like Man, are prone to vanity, jealousy, snootiness and impishness.

The sea lion, for example, loves to exhibit its cleverness and is positively miserable if it can't show off before a crowd, whether the crowd be fellow sea lions or people. It is so vain that it applauds itself. The only thing that depresses a sea lion more than not being able to show off is to have to stand politely on the sidelines while another sea lion is strutting its stuff.

Often there are startling personality contrasts, within a family. The little weasel probably has the nastiest disposition in the entire world. It is pure ferocity personified, a bloodthirsty murderer who throws itself at its victims (often many times larger than itself) in a paroxysm of fury.

In contrast the otter, a member of the weasel family, is supercharged with weasel energy but discharges it in fun-loving frolic and amiability. It is the playboy of the animal world.

The three Great Apes—the orangutan, the gorilla and the chimpanzee—are all too intelligent for Man's peace of mind. But all three have strikingly different personalities.

An orang is sweet, lovable and quiet. The first human investigators were so infatuated with the orang that they claimed it was the brightest creature in the animal kingdom. Now it appears that it is not—not quite.

In the past we have seen so much high-powered publicity about Gargantua and King Kong that we think of the gorilla as a savage, limb-tearing brute. Actually, psychologists find, the gorilla is a quiet, shy introvert, immaculately tidy in everything it does. The gorilla is affectionate by nature and usually becomes so fond of its human zoo keepers that it cannot conceal its jealousy when the keeper is attending to other animals.

The third Great Ape, the chimpanzee, is the wise guy, the talkative extrovert. He's a bit scatterbrained and boisterous, but incredibly ingenious when he puts his mind to a problem. The chimp has a Legionnaire's sense of humor and delights in knocking hats off ladies, and in making monkeys of his human investigators.

We see another personality contrast in the rhinoceros and the hippopotamus. The rhino is invariably truculent and bad-tempered. The slightest disturbance in its neighborhood sets it rampaging through the jungle. In contrast, the hippopotamus—which children at the zoo often confuse with the rhino—is extremely placid and agreeable.

Even Man's best friends, the dog, the cat and the horse, have distinctive personality traits. The dog is doggedly loyal and pathetically eager to please. His outstanding trait is his dumb devotion to Man. He seems so bright and full of tricks, yet he can act like a rattleheaded sap when anyone attempts to measure his IQ.

The cat is far more independent than the dog even though she accepts the support of Man. She is standoffish, no hand-licker. It is hard to think of the cat in masculine terms because the behavior of all cats is so humanly feminine. All cats—from pussy to Leo, King of the Jungle—are dainty about their persons and somewhat secretive.

We all know that the horse is noble. But few of us also realize that the horse is high-strung and can act like a hysterical fool when a leaf flutters by. The horse has been glorified by so many writers and movies that few of us know that the horse, for all its reputed brilliance and power, is actually not too bright, as animals go.

The psychologists, and other scientifically trained observers, have reached some startling conclusions about the real intelligence and personalities of many of the animals we see or read about every day.

They have reached some solid conclusions about the question, "Can animals talk?" They have found which animals live under dictatorships, which under democracies, and which under apparent anarchy.

In the following pages I shall try to unfold for you some of the more surprising findings about the way animals really behave.

The Human Side
of
Animals

———

(Original title: ANIMAL IQ)

1. How Do You Spot a Wise Animal?

THE problem of obtaining reliable information about the wisdom of animals is fascinating because every investigator is confronted with so many pitfalls. Gauging the IQ of a horse or a hippopotamus is a tricky business, in fact much more tricky than gauging the IQ of a man.

For one thing there are many people who want to give you dubious information—with the best intentions. In America today there are 600 different societies dedicated to protecting or promoting some animal.

The dog has millions of fans who will rush forward with stories to prove how bright their own dog is. One fan reported to a psychologist that he saw a dog save another dog from drowning by grabbing a long stick in his teeth and using it to pull in the drowning dog.

Our psychologist spent months duplicating this situation under laboratory conditions. He took two dogs to a stream with a steep bank, laid plenty of long sticks near by and then threw one dog into the water. The dog on the bank dashed around excitedly but was never able to offer any help. Usually the psychologist had to haul the distressed dog out. He repeated the experiments with most of the dogs in his neighborhood. His sad conclusion: "Not proven."

During the early decades of this century many investigators gathered evidence on the wisdom of animals in order to test Darwin's theory about the close kinship of other animals to Man. Most of the investigators tended to be overeager. They advertised that they were seeking examples of animal wisdom and offered financial rewards for choice examples. They were deluged with fantastic stories of animal genius that came third hand from "veteran trappers," missionaries and "natives." One investigator reported earnestly that he had heard of a bird that had splinted its broken leg with sticks and mud.

Another problem in trying to size up animals for their intelligence is that their behavior is often deceiving, especially to an unwary, untrained eye. People who have watched a sea lion perform on the stage will assure you that the sea lion is a musical genius. It can toot out "My Country 'Tis of Thee . . ." and even *Yankee Doodle*.

What the average person in the audience does not realize is that the animal is playing not "by ear" but "by position." It would do just as well if all the horns in its battery made the same noise. When bribed by sufficient fish, a well-trained sea lion will go through a given order of motions. If the horns were placed on a vertical rather than a horizontal line the sea lion would be utterly stumped, and would have to be completely retrained.

The biggest pitfall for unwary investigators, however, is the danger of confusing instinctive acts with "thinking." There are animals that exhibit real reasoning power, but there are many others that perform astounding acts of complexity and seeming wisdom purely by instinct.

Nature has built their ingenuity into their genes as an unthinking habit pattern to enable them to survive as a species. Thus their wisdom is not an individually acquired thing but is the Wisdom of Nature. (That of course does not make it any less remarkable.)

Let us look at some of the more amazing examples of this Wisdom of Nature.

The mole has an ingenious technique for assuring itself a steady supply of fresh food. Its favorite food is moist, wiggly earthworms. If the mole killed the worms when they were captured the worms would soon shrivel and become distasteful. So, instead of killing the worms, the mole simply nips off the head end of each worm. This does not kill the worm but makes it incapable of burrowing—and thus escaping. In doing this the moles are evidently impelled by an inborn instinct.

Likewise skunks bite through the brains of frogs they capture. This paralyzes the frogs but does not kill them. Thus the frogs may be stored away so that the baby skunks may have fresh food.

Sea gulls have a technique for opening the tough shells of clams that often amazes human witnesses, and is apparently instinctive. The gulls take the shell-enclosed clams high up into the air, drop them on rocks to crack the shells, then swoop down to pick out the morsels.

Then there are certain instinctive acts animals use for protecting themselves that show the wizardry of Nature. The African wart hog always *backs* into its hole (instead of going in head first) so that its vulnerable posterior is not exposed to any leopard that may be lurking in the brush.

Another animal, the giant anteater, doesn't have enough brains in its head to fill a peanut. But when it sleeps, it curls up in a tight ball and drapes its giant grayish-brown tail over its body, so that the whole mass looks like a heap of dead leaves.

Nature has endowed the pied-billed grebe (or "Helldiver") with a great deal of inborn ingenuity in concealing its marshland nest. Whenever the Helldiver spies an enemy approaching, it pulls a mat of rotting vegetation over its nest and submerges in the water without making a ripple, and reappears 100 feet away. It also pulls the mat over its nest whenever it goes away in search of food.

One of the most astounding acts performed by any bird is part of the behavior pattern of the honey-guide bird of central Africa. This creature is so rare that it is difficult to say just what goes on in its mind during its amazing performance, but presumably it acts from instinct.

At any rate, it teams up with ground animals to get its food. Whenever it spots a bees' nest in the forest the honey-guide bird goes tearing out over the forest emitting a harsh, distinctive noise, "nyeteh-nyeteh," which apparently is produced by the vibration of its tail feathers.

After bugling the news that it has found a bees' nest it leads the alerted animals to the nest. The ground animals destroy the nest and eat the honey. After they have gone, the honey-guide can then gorge itself on its favorite food—beeswax.

The world's foremost authority on army ants, T.C. Schneirla of New York University and the American Museum of Natural History has said that the army ant has "a limited capacity for learning. By far the greater part of its behavior pattern is written in its genes." Yet he reports that the army ants have domesticated animals just as we have cows, and they also have slave ants. Futhermore, they cultivate agricultural crops, and carry parasols on hot days!

The behavior of certain fish, birds, and mammals is still a great mystery to scientists. Consider the amazing migration of Egyptian eels. These eels found near Egypt migrate 4,000 miles to their spawning ground deep in the ocean near the West Indies. To get to the Atlantic Ocean they must first cross the Mediterranean and find the narrow strait of Gibraltar. How do they do it? Science still doesn't know. But it is not likely that individual brains have much to do with it.

At Pennsylvania State College, my old friend Professor Henry Yeagley spent many years studying the amazing flights of homing pigeons. Finally he solved the mystery. He suspected that pigeons could sense the earth's magnetism. When he attached light magnets to the wings of the pigeons, they became confused and lost their way home.

Magnetism alone, however, could not account for the pigeon's ability to "feel" its way home. The earth's magnetic force increases steadily from equator to the poles but at any latitude it is the same all the way around the globe. There must be, he decided, a second force. Finally he concluded it was the Coriolis force, which is created by the spinning of the earth. This force likewise increases from the equator to the poles—but along different lines.

Pigeons, it seems, can feel the combined pull of these two forces. Professor Yeagley noticed that in only one other spot in the United States was the combined pull of these two forces exactly the same as at Penn State. That spot is near Kearney, Nebraska. So he took his trained pigeons to Nebraska and let them loose. Sure enough they beelined for Kearney!

All of these cases I have cited of remarkable animal behavior appear to involve instinctive acts inherent in the race rather than individual brain-power. We get vivid evidence of instinctive actions when we place animals out of their natural setting.

Wild dogs through the ages have always made a sleeping place at night by turning around and around in the tall grass to make a comfortable bed. But notice your dog when it lies down on your living-room rug to take a snooze. It will still go instinctively around and around.

Squirrels in the wild bury their nuts. If you give a tame squirrel nuts in your living room it will take them into a corner and go through the motions of burying them, even to the extent of stamping down "earth" on them.

Slaughterhouses take advantage of the sheep's instinct to follow the leader by using a goat to lead sheep to slaughter. These instinctive acts of animals, while remarkable in themselves, are a far cry from acts of individual reasoning of which certain animals are capable. The best way to test an animal's reasoning power is to confront it with a problem it has never faced before. If it has never faced the problem, obviously instinct can't be involved in a solution.

In the jungle, for example, there are no boxes. Yet if you put a chimpanzee in a yard where a banana is suspended beyond his reach, and where boxes are within sight, the chimpanzee will assemble the boxes, pile them on top of each other until he has a platform high enough to enable him to reach the banana! That, all scientists agree, involves real, individual reasoning.

It is hard for Man to conceive of the world animals live in, with their different senses. We tend to assume that the animal's brain is a reflection of our own, in miniature. With mammals that is true to a certain degree. But with birds there is no development whatever of that part of the brain which in humans is devoted to thought. And the structure of the brains of insects is so utterly different from ours that we can only make wild guesses as to what goes on inside their little heads.

With many of the lower animals, such as birds and insects, the life span is so short that there is little time for much learning. The behavior patterns that will insure survival must be largely built in.

LAMBS BEING LED TO SLAUGHTER

Meat packers take advantage of the instinct of sheep to follow a leader. Here an experienced old Judas goat leads a herd straight to the butchering pits.

The young spider, for example, builds a perfect cob-web the first time it tries, and without instruction.

In one test weaver birds were deprived of any nesting material for four generations. Yet when the birds born into the fifth generation were provided with nesting materials they wove their elaborate nest perfectly.

That is instinct in action. Many of the lower animals, birds, reptiles, insects, etc. are capable of very complex behavior patterns based on instinct, but are unable to profit much by experience. That is, they can't *learn* how to do much they don't already know automatically. Their capabilities for learning from experience are fairly limited, and their ability to reason is nil.

As we come up the evolutionary scale of animals, however, we find that certain creatures, especially the mammals, can *learn* a good deal. Learning is a more advanced type of animal intelligence than instinctive action, and it involves modifying instinct by experience.

It would be extremely difficult, if not impossible, to housebreak a chicken. But a puppy readily learns to be

clean in a house if he finds that he gets his bottom paddled every time he slips up. Likewise the puppy will learn to roll over or stand on his hind legs if he is rewarded with a bone or a pat.

Finally, above learning we come to the supreme type of animal intelligence which is *reasoning*. This always consists in devising the solution to a problem which has not previously been mastered through trial-and-error learning. The chimpanzee, for example, employs reason when, without previous trial-and-error effort, it stacks boxes in order to reach the banana.

We have, then, three distinctly different types of intelligence revealed in animal behavior: instinctive actions, learned actions and reasoned actions. Let us keep them clear in our minds as we consider the prodigious efforts psychologists are making to probe the minds of some of our nimble-witted and dull-witted creatures.

2. Psychologists vs. "Dumb" Animals

NE afternoon a wild, unearthly roar broke the placid calm of New York City's Bronx Zoo. People in the zoo were startled and many hurried toward the spot where the noise was originating.

They found that four psychologists were responsible for the bedlam. These men had been testing the IQ of a young lady elephant at the zoo by playing the old shell game on her.

Two strings led under a box, which was dark on one side, light on the other. The elephant knew that a lovely apple was attached to one string. But which? She eyed the strings hesitantly, pulled the wrong one. No apple! She became excited, then outraged. She trumpeted and lunged in a terrifying tantrum.

When her IQ testing was resumed, after a considerable cooling-off period, each of the psychologists nervously gripped the fence, prepared to vault it in a flash. To their immense relief, however, she put her mind intently to the problem and managed on the first try to score. It was not long before her pulling average was so favorable that she was eating the psychologists out of apples.

She is just one of many animals at the zoo whose minds, habits and love lives have been explored by the psychologists. Often these comparative psychologists, who are drawn from various leading universities, have slept right at the zoo, not far from the tiger cages.

As they have staged their battles of wits with the animals, throngs of children often surge by. The youngsters usually root for the animals, but show their fair-mindedness by tossing peanuts to animals and the good-natured psychologists alike.

If you walk past the gorilla cages you may see a psychologist furiously taking notes as two gorillas stage an uproarious mock battle in which they pull hair, and hurl each other about with the cross-body flings that professional wrestlers are so fond of using.

Or if you stroll past the field where a herd of small deer graze you may see psychologists throwing small sponge balls covered with wet paint at them. The psychologists may be studying the social order of the deer and are finding it hard to tell one deer from another. So they mark them by throwing wet paint balls of different colors at the various deer. The spots will stay on for two weeks.

Some of the experiments at the Bronx Zoo for the New York Zoological Society have been under the on-the-spot direction of Hunter College's Dr. Bernard Riess, one of America's leading animal behaviorists.

Throughout the country from Yale to Wisconsin to California at least a hundred psychologists have been busy trying to get inside the minds of animals, both wild and domesticated. The investigations are far from complete, but the picture that seems to be emerging from all these experiments should impel us to treat some of our animal neighbors, especially the wild ones, with greater respect. The psychologists, for example, have rarely built a maze that some animal has not been able to master.

From a scientific point of view these animal behavior studies are important not only because they give us a better understanding of animals but because they are also throwing light on Man's own emotional make-up. In Man's evolutionary development his early ancestors presumably passed through some of the stages closely resembling stages various animals are in today.

As a part of the exhaustive studies, some psychologists are even studying animals before they are old enough to be born. They operate on the mother, remove the fetal animal and keep it in a saline solution while studying its movements.

At Columbia University there has been a psychology class in which each student was assigned a white rat at the beginning of the term and conducted tests with it throughout the year. Some of the students became so fond of their rats that they took them home with them, and named them after their girl friends.

The testing of animals can be an exciting or hilarious experience, especially if the animals are chimpanzees. Dr. Herbert Birch of New York has spent a good many hours studying the apes at the Bronx Zoo. Once he had to wrestle his way out of a cage full of husky chimps that felt he had pulled a fast one on them. "Sometimes," he said, "the animals grasp the psychologist rather than the problem."

Apes think up many ways to harass the psychologists. Dr. Birch became an expert at ducking flattened tin cans hurled with frightening accuracy by gorillas, and jets of water squirted from the mouths of playful chimpanzees.

He reported that the normal accurate squirting range of a chimp is about 12 feet. He found, however, that he could not depend on that. One chimp discovered that it could increase its range up to 20 feet by taking a flying leap against the bars of the cage. The impact of the bars on the chimp's belly would add at least eight more feet to its firing range.

These showers never particularly bothered Dr. Birch. He would continue his investigation with single-minded

devotion even though drenched. But one day his wife, who dropped by in a new dress to watch him work, was soaked by a chimp. And she was not amused. She suggested to Dr. Birch that if he was so smart he ought to figure out a way to outwit the chimps.

Dr. Birch devoted considerable scientific thought to the matter and arrived at a solution. Whenever he saw a chimpanzee tanking up on water he ran up to the cage and spit at the chimp first! This offensive action invariably dismayed the chimp into opening its mouth in consternation. The water then drooled harmlessly down its own chin.

Frequently, testing a chimp can be a surprising experience. One psychologist rigged up an experiment in which a banana was suspended in the usual fashion in mid-air about five feet beyond the chimp's reach. Then he scattered some boxes on the ground near by.

GENIUS AT WORK

You don't get bananas without thinking. This quick-witted chimpanzee figured out that only by stacking the boxes could he climb high enough to reach the fruit.

The problem the psychologist had set up, of course, was this: would the chimp (whose name was Sultan) be smart enough to stack the boxes to make a platform? Sultan took a look at the banana, trotted over to the psychologist, grabbed him by the seat of the pants and hauled him to a spot directly beneath the banana.

Sultan's Big Idea finally dawned on the psychologist. As Sultan vaulted the psychologist's shoulders the man bent forward quickly. Thus Sultan could not

HOW WOULD YOU HAVE DONE IT?

Another problem which confronted this really brilliant chimpanzee was to obtain the banana hung from the ceiling. To aid him he had nothing but a long pole. The chimp took one look at the banana, then stood the pole directly under the prize, climbed aloft and jumped down with the unbruised fruit.

reach the banana after all. Sultan got down, complaining, took the psychologist again by the seat of the pants and with both hands pushed the man into an erect position. Then Sultan vaulted to his shoulders and was able to grab the banana.

In a similar test a banana was suspended in mid-air and the only implement left available in the yard was a long pole. The psychologist had wondered if the ape would be smart enough to use the pole to knock the banana down to the ground. That's the way the psychologist would have gone about it.

The chimp picked up the pole all right, but instead of using it as a stick he stood the pole on the ground directly beneath the banana. Then he zipped up the pole hand over hand before it could fall down, grabbed the banana and leaped to the ground! Possibly a pole has different associative connotations to a man and to an ape, but at any rate the ape's solution was far superior to the man's because the banana was captured *unbruised*.

Psychologists tell the story of a colleague who spent several days rigging up a soundproof room filled with mechanical toys. He led a chimpanzee into the room, then tiptoed out. How would the chimp react to the various gadgets when alone? The psychologist went to get his notebook and pencil, then stooped down to the keyhole to observe the chimp's activities with the toys.

What he observed instead was one bright eye observing *him* from the other side of the keyhole! This story could not be verified, but all the psychologists I consulted about it agreed that it was certainly plausible.

One of the most fascinating aspects of animal-testing is watching how animals behave while they are being tested. A chimpanzee named Mimi became so keyed up that she developed a hand-washing compulsion before it was time to go into the testing room. She would go to her push-button water fountain and cool her hairy paddies time after time. That, you might say, is "only human." I've noticed that students in my university have spent an extraordinary amount of time at the water fountains and washrooms before examinations.

Another chimp, Koko, was bothered by chronic indigestion on testing days. And if his first attempts to solve a problem failed, he was likely to fly into a tantrum, hop around on one foot, and pound the walls.

Some of the chimps, when baffled, seem to itch all over. They fidget, squirm and whimper. One chimp, when frustrated, actually turned its back on the problem, just as we humans, as psychiatrists well know, often try to turn our backs, figuratively, on frustrating situations.

An orangutan named Julius, when especially discouraged, would bump his head hard against the floor. This reaction was strikingly similar to that of a seven-year-old boy who, when baffled by a tough multiple choice problem, banged his head on the wall. When the lad was asked why he banged his head, he explained ruefully: "I want to stir things up."

When the famed Robert Yerkes of the Yale Primate Laboratories was testing Wendy, a temperamental chimp, he ran into difficulties. He had rigged up a revolving table which Wendy was to turn until she came to the same color that he held up. It was a color-matching test. If she gave the right answer she could take her breakfast from the table. But on this day she erred. A wire screen slammed down. No breakfast!

Wendy was furious. As Dr. Yerkes led her back into her cage where there were three other chimps, Wendy grabbed his hand and bit it and screamed for help. The other three husky chimps piled onto him and pretended to bite him.

"Afterward," Dr. Yerkes reported, "all of them but Wendy acted apologetic and ashamed."

The gorilla, in contrast to chimps, does not take much

interest in tests. However, it shows little frustration
when it can't solve a problem (and get the reward).

Monkeys, which are somewhat lower down on the
evolutionary scale than apes, work quite hard at tests,
especially if they know the psychologist personally. And
they tend to become cocky and boisterous if they master
a problem.

But a frustrated monkey is apt to raise havoc with
experimental apparatus. Many try to throw the whole
business out the window. One psychologist found he
could conduct his tests smoothly only if he bolted the
apparatus to the floor.

In another instance a psychologist trained a monkey
to swap marbles for morsels of food. When this was
learned, the psychologist began accepting marbles without giving anything in return. The first time this happened the monkey, named Trader, acted puzzled. The
second time he showed irritation. The third time it happened Trader was outraged, howled in monkey language that he was being cheated and, screaming at the
top of his lungs, began beating the rug with his heels.

Even white rats can become temperamental when
they are baffled. Prof. Schneirla has reported that one
rat that lost its way in a maze finally sat down despond-
ently in a runway and began biting its fingernails.

At Columbia the white rats were taught that if they
would hold a metal bar down, the bright light above the
cage would go off and stop hurting their eyes. One rat
sat for half an hour holding the bar down with his paw
in order to keep that confounded light out of his eyes.

A monkey at the Yale Institute for Human Relations
was continually harassed by the clanging of a bell outside its cage. The monkey was almost a nervous wreck
before it finally learned that it could end the din by
reaching through its cage and pulling a lever—a somewhat more complicated operation than the rat's performance.

One of the big problems that confronts any psychologist who wants to test animals is to find an incentive that will stir his subjects to put forth their very best efforts. You can tell a high school student that he is going to flunk out of school if he does not pass his algebra exam, but what can you tell a chicken? Dogs will do their best just for a pat on the head. And some chimps will work just for the mental stimulation and the pleasure they get from making a monkey out of the psychologist. But unfortunately, practically all other animals need a much more concrete incentive. With each animal the incentive may be different.

Food will often work, but not just everyday food. Unless the animals are desperately hungry, you have got to find what they consider to be desserts. Monkeys, for example, love grapes, so most tests with monkeys start with that simple fact. The dog-faced baboons at the Bronx Zoo willingly eat carrots and lettuce in their regular diet, but they wouldn't work for them on tests. "Why work for spinach?" they shrug. Only when the psychologists enticed them with cherries and grapes would they put forth their best efforts.

A psychologist at another university dangled a banana before a chimp and appeared to put it inside the box the chimp was to try to open. But instead, by a slight of hand, the psychologist substituted lettuce, which the chimp eats but does not love. When the chimp finally managed to open the box and found the lettuce he was surprised and disappointed. He threw the lettuce over his shoulder and began turning the box upside down in search of that banana.

At Yale an experimenter put two white rats in identical cages side by side. If either would learn to press a little iron bar, a food pellet would drop into its cage. One of the rats was very hungry. The other had just had a full meal.

The hungry rat, eagerly exploring his cage for possible food, soon accidentally hit the bar. He gobbled the food that dropped out without realizing the cause and effect involved, and kept chasing hungrily around the cage. After hitting the bar (and getting food) several times, he got the idea and soon was emptying his food machine of all its food pellets.

Meanwhile the full-bellied rat in the cage a few inches away was lying quietly in its corner digesting its food and paying no attention whatever to its slot machine.

But that is not the end of the story. This second rat's cage had a metallic bottom that could be electrified. When this rat was given a mild shock it leaped to its feet and danced wildly about the electrified floor. Accidentally it hit a little iron bar and the shock stopped.

Here we are back to the two basic incentives: reward and punishment. The interesting thing, however, is that the rat that was punished by the shock learned to press its lever much faster than the hungry rat learned to press its food lever!

Another interesting finding about food is that while you get better results by starving an animal a little, if an animal is deprived of food or water for much longer than 24 hours, it does worse, rather than better, on tests.

Then there are some animals that cannot be motivated by food at all. This is particularly the case with reptiles. Snakes, for example, feed irregularly, often at very long intervals, and they aren't interested in food again until the last meal has been digested. Apparently stomach contractions arouse the snake to begin food-hunting.

IT'S A LONG WAY TO A DRINK

This comparatively slow-witted turtle learned by trial and error that he had to solve the maze-on-stilts before he could reach the water. As you can see, no other method of approach would have made it possible for him to enter the glass bowl.

Dr. Riess recently had some alligators he wanted to test on his maze at the American Museum of Natural History. But he was stymied because he couldn't find any satisfactory incentive, since alligators don't eat regularly.

He had the same problem with his turtles. Dr. Riess's turtle finally mastered a simple elevated maze test after 39 yawn-filled, meandering trials. During every trial Dr. Riess had to battle to keep himself awake. Whenever he found himself dozing he gave the turtle a mild hotfoot with his Bunsen burner.

In testing ants on a simple maze, Dr. Schneirla found that the ants would learn the path much more quickly when they were staggering home to their nest with a load of food than when they were going out fresh and unencumbered.

An experimenter testing apes found that chimps could be motivated by competition. When a chimp saw an-

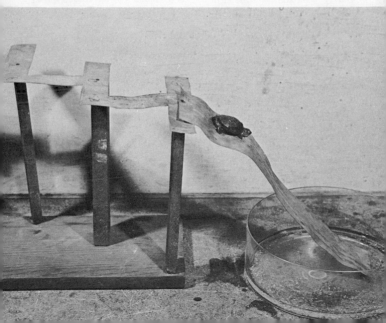

other ape about to get a prize the chimp would renew his own efforts with a great bustle of activity.

Several psychologists rigged up a device by means of which an incentive could be placed in one compartment and to reach that compartment white rats had to cross over an electrified grill that gave them a small shock. In the incentive compartment they placed food for hungry rats and water for thirsty rats. They found that animals suffering from thirst would brave the grill more readily than animals suffering from hunger.

Another interesting study has been made of incentives that impel racing pigeons to do their best. It was found that a hen puts forth her greatest effort when setting on eggs or on tiny youngsters.

With male birds it was found that jealousy can be a tremendous incentive. The experimenter placed a strange, handsome male in a nest with one cock's lady friend before the cock's very eyes, then took the frantically jealous husband cock to a point many miles away and let him loose. He beelined home in record-shattering time!

3. Stumping the Experts with a Puzzle Box

NCE you have found an incentive that an animal will really work hard for, you still face the monumental problem of devising a test that will probe the animal's intelligence and yet be fair to all contenders. This is the toughest problem a psychologist has to face.

After all, a porcupine or even a monkey cannot read or write (so far as we know). Furthermore, only the primates have hands in the sense that we have. The dog has four legs, the chicken two legs, the snake crawls, the fish swims. How can you devise a test that will give all an even break?

In recent decades many psychologists have put their brains to this problem. A few tests have emerged as favorites. It is important that you know what they can do, and the strengths and shortcomings of each.

One of the great favorites for many years has been the maze, where the animal, in order to get to its goal rapidly, must learn to avoid blind alleys. Dozens of animals, including cockroaches, cowbirds, toads, turtles, bluebirds and snakes, have mastered fairly simple mazes.

At the American Museum of Natural History's Animal Behavior Laboratory Dr. Riess and his associates stacked up several small-fry animals against each other in a fairly involved type of maze, where six wrong turns into blind alleys could be made. Of the six competing animals they found that a curious little kitten came out on top. Here is their ranking in descending order from best to poorest:

> Kitten
> White Rat
> Fish (guppies and sword-tails)
> Guinea Pig
> Chick
> Turtle

In practically all psychological tests that have been made, the guinea pig has come out well behind the white rat even though the two look a lot alike. The guinea pig's relative stupidity is laid to the fact that after conception this animal becomes fully developed in an extremely short period of time. Thus it doesn't have time to learn much. It operates pretty much on an automatic, instinctive basis.

The white rat on the other hand has a fairly agile, ingenious mind when it comes to figuring out mazes. At the museum, rats learned mazes with as many as 25 blind alleys.

A maze, while a handy device to make comparative tests with small animals of a low order, has its shortcomings for measuring the IQs of higher mammals and Man. This was dramatically illustrated by a startling experiment carried on at a Southern university.

There two psychologists set out to pit 27 white rats against 38 college students (19 girls, 19 men). They constructed a long elevated maze. The rats could run along it, and blindfolded students could follow it by running their hands along the path.

WORRIED KITTEN

That stop watch would make you nervous, too! Here Dr. Bernard Riess of the American Museum of Natural History put a kitten through the maze test.

As far as possible all conditions were held the same for both sets of contestants. It was felt necessary to blindfold the students so that they could not see the overall pattern. However, the students, unlike the rats, were not starved a little beforehand. Also, while food was held out to the rats as an inducement, the only incentive for the students was to uphold the dignity of the human race.

The results were pretty embarrassing. The white rats did clearly better than the students. They could run through the maze without making a single error in fewer trips than the students had to take. It took the students three times as long to go through the maze three consecutive times without error as it took the rats.

Only in one particular did the human contestants excel. That was when all the contestants were given the same test again after a month's lapse of time. Then the students were able to relearn the maze with less difficulty than the rats.

The results of this experiment laid bare one big weakness of the maze: it measures only one type of intelligence and that is the lower intermediary learning type. The college students had no opportunity to put their reasoning powers to work. At each intersection, on the first trip, a blind guess had to be made. And on succeeding trips the problem was to learn the right turns by memorization, as you learn your ABC's. The students were given no opportunity to apply their presumably superior reasoning powers by making logical deductions.

But even so, the experiment was a sobering event.

The second major device used for probing animal minds is the Problem Box. Here the animal is placed either inside or outside a wire box. The trick is that it must learn to open the door of the box in order to reach food which is in sight. The door can be opened by pushing down a simple lever or taut string, jerking at a chain, stepping on a foot pedal, tearing away a paper seal or some other simple brain-teasing movement.

Porcupines, pigeons, squirrels, crows, groundhogs, cats, dogs, and in fact practically all furry or feathered creatures have strutted their stuff on these boxes. The boxes are not practical, however, for reptiles, fish, bugs and toads.

The porcupines, which are pretty clever if obnoxious little animals, learned to open puzzle boxes requiring the use of levers, raising a hook . . . removing a plug . . . turning a button, and combinations of these. And cebus monkeys learned to open boxes with a hook and eye to be separated . . . bars to be lifted . . . strings to be pulled . . . plugs to be removed . . . wires that required unwinding . . . loops to be lifted from a nail.

RABBIT RIDDLE

This rabbit is trying to remember which white-circled pedal must be depressed to open the puzzle box containing the carrot.

Psychologists have argued among themselves over how much intelligence is involved in opening a problem box. Normally the door is opened the first time by dumb luck, as when a bird happens to light on the string. Then gradually an association is made between hitting the string and getting food. Whether the bird ever comprehends the mechanics involved is disputed.

In this test a more active animal such as a kitten naturally has some advantage over a slow-moving animal such as the porcupine.

Another drawback of this is that manipulating mechanical devices is easier for some animals than for others. In order partly to eliminate this difficulty many experimenters began turning to the Jenkins Box, where conditions can be kept constant for all mammals and birds. The animal simply has to step on a colored disk to open the door. And the test can be made more difficult by adding disks.

In one test the animals had to walk back and forth in sequence over three disks to open the lock. The guinea pig never got the idea of this at all and only succeeded where it had to step on a single disk. The white rat learned to step on two disks, and a kitten got as high as seven disks. But the champion was the cebus monkey which succeeded in opening the box, when he was required to step on disks in proper order, 22 times!

An even more difficult variation is the puzzle box which can be opened only by unfastening a series of locks in a *definite order*. The second one cannot be freed until the first lock is mastered. This is really a postgraduate problem for animal geniuses. In such a test monkeys were able to operate five locks in the required order. It was found that monkeys became "lock-conscious" and spotted a new lock almost as soon as it was introduced on a box and went directly to work on it without wasteful trial and error.

In most puzzle box tests it would be unfair to pit animals against Man because human beings are trained from infancy to open doors, push light buttons, etc.

Now we come to a third popular—and very simple—technique used by scientists to challenge the ingenuity of animals. This consists in putting food in front of an animal, just out of reach, and forcing the animal to take a roundabout route to reach it. This is a trickier and more penetrating test than it appears.

One easy way to stage this is to separate an animal such as a chicken from a pile of wheat by a short stretch of chicken wire fence. The chicken will make a spectacle of itself beating itself against the fence trying to get through, even though the fence ends in plain view a few feet away. Only after much frantic dashing back and forth, all the time keeping an anxious eye on the wheat, will the chicken find its way around the fence.

A dog separated from a bone will get the idea of trot-

FAST THINKER GETS PRIZE

Dumb animals—such as the chicken—never get the idea of taking a roundabout route to get food. The dog caught on, but only after the monkey had showed him the way.

ting around the fence somewhat faster. And a four-year-old child separated from a doll will almost instantly get the idea of going around the fence.

A variation of this test is to put the animal on a long leash tied to a stake. The leash is trailed around a second stake, which prevents the animal from getting enough slack to reach the food a few feet ahead. A dog will usually strain at the leash a long time before getting the idea of going back around the second stake. On the other hand, a monkey sized the situation up fairly rapidly, went back and lifted the leash over the obstacle stake.

Professor Frank Beach, the Yale psychologist, told in *Natural History* of an octopus that was separated from a prawn by a large pane of glass. He said:

"It would seem a simple matter for the octopus to move sideways just far enough to pass around the edge of the glass. But this would mean moving away from the visible prey, and such a course of action is too much for the cephalopod 'mind.' "

The octopus and the chicken (and to a lesser extent the dog) are limited by a one-track mind. They lack adaptability, and that lack makes them incapable of higher reasoning. Here's how Professor Beach explained it:

"The ability to give up one line of attack and shift to a new one is quite limited in animals that belong below the mammals in the evolutionary scale." (Mammals are warm-blooded creatures that nourish their young on milk.)

Professor Beach went on to add that on occasion grown men sometimes get in a rut and act like chickens in their insistence upon trying to cope with a novel problem in an old, unsuitable way.

Scientists have devised tests that are designed to isolate higher types of intelligence than are involved in simple learning through association by repetitions (such as you get in the maze). We have already mentioned the shell game used on the elephant and the box stacking problem used on primates.

One technique is the delayed response. If an animal sees food buried or placed in one of two boxes, how long can it be delayed and still go directly to the food when it has the opportunity? This tests the animal's ability to substitute, as a stimulus, an idea for the food itself. Rats can be delayed only a few seconds but a chimpanzee that saw a pear being buried was able to go directly to the spot after being delayed 16½ hours. Another type of advanced IQ test is the "multiple choice" problem. For example, there is a series of compartments. The food is placed first in the box on the extreme left, then in the extreme right in regular alternation. Of all the animals tested on this, only the monkey seemed to grasp the principle of alternation.

I should like to mention, in passing, experiments that psychologists are carrying on with animals to test their emotional make-up. Many animals are being subjected to emotional strains, often to the point where they become clearly neurotic. It is hoped that the data gathered from these tests will supply psychiatrists and psychologists with valuable information for the solution of the emotional problems of human beings.

In one test, for example, it was found that when a baby chick is reared in solitary confinement it becomes wildly eccentric.

Professor Norman Maier of the University of Michigan rigged up a test in which a rat was taught to jump at cards from a high platform. There were two cards. The one with the white circle would fall aside when the rat jumped against it and let the rat into a food cupboard. In contrast, the black-circled card stayed put. This not only gave the rat a bump on the nose but forced it to fall into a net, a nasty experience.

The rat quickly learned to jump only at the white-circled card. But then Professor Maier pulled a switch.

He would place the food alternately behind one, then the other. The rat was unable to cope with this new problem and after several bad bumps, refused to jump. Professor Maier then forced the rat to jump by applying a strong jet of air to its posterior.

Soon he had a very neurotic, frustrated rat. This neurotic rat fell into the stereotyped habit of jumping at the card on the left, no matter which color circle showed.

The important point is that neither rewards, punishment nor training could break this habit. The rat's mind congealed. Professor Maier could take away the card on the right, and show the rat the food behind it. The wretched white rat would look at the food, sniff at it longingly—then leap and bump its head against the card on the *left*.

Professor Maier suggested that perhaps human beings who become frustrated by problems which are too complicated for them to solve, react in much the same way. He wonders if trouble-making nations in the world are often acting not with clear-cut objections in mind but rather out of frustration.

"To what extent," he asked, "are our behaviors frustrated reactions rather than problem-solving reactions? Can a frustrated world solve its problems?"

That's an interesting question which delegates to the United Nations might well take up.

4. Wisdom of the Birds and the Bees

SCIENTISTS today are finding that practically every living organism is capable of some degree of learning. But the degree varies fantastically.

Here we will consider some of the more surprising evidences of wisdom in the so-called "lower animals." In the biologists' view the lower animals are those below the mammal (warm-blooded, milk-feeding species) on the evolutionary scale.

Near the bottom of the scale of the lower animals are the worms, insects and other creatures that do not have a spine (invertebrates). Next come the fishes . . . then the amphibians such as the frog . . . then the reptiles such as the snake and alligator . . . and finally the birds.

Surprisingly, however, these lower animals don't always follow the expected order in their performance on IQ tests. The lowly ant for example, has proven itself to be a whiz in learning a maze.

In one test ants mastered a maze having *six* blind alleys after only 35 trips through it. Ants, in fact, have learned mazes with more blind alleys than have even been mastered by any fish, amphibian or reptile! Psychologists hasten to explain that this does not necessarily mean the ant has superior learning ability. They say that the ant is greatly aided, in solving a maze, by its very acute senses and the ease and quickness with which it can move around.

31

Even the earthworm, one of the lowliest of all living creatures, has proven itself capable of mastering a very simple maze. Some psychologists rigged up a simple T maze where only one choice has to be learned. The worm was placed in a moist dark chamber. The other alley was blind. If the worm went there it received a mild electric shock.

With the stage thus set, the cover was taken off the chamber containing the worm. The hot uncomfortable light impelled the worm to wiggle off toward the intersection in search of darkness. After 150 trials several worms learned consistently to make the right turn.

Bees, it has been discovered, have an amazing ability for estimating lapses of time. If someone asks you what time it is and you haven't seen a clock all day how close can you come to estimating the time? Can you say "It is 10:28" and be within two or three minutes of being correct? Bees, if they could talk, could apparently do this.

There are flowers that open and close at definite times of day while in bloom. Bees quickly learn the precise moment when they are to come for the nectar. Test-bees with paint spots on their bodies have been observed arriving at a flower day after day at almost exactly the same moment.

Let us now move a step up the evolutionary scale to the fish. Experimenters have found that the fish has a remarkable eye for form. In one test the fish was able to get food if it swam toward a circle but could not get food if it swam toward an oval. The test fish learned to go consistently to the circle, and they even learned to distinguish between the letters R and L.

These results suggest it is quite possible, as many old fishermen suspect, that a fish can in time learn to recognize, and avoid, lures if they follow a set pattern. Also, psychologists have confirmed that some fish appear to be much smarter than others. The trout, for example, appears to be vastly more intelligent and wary—in its ability to avoid traps—than the herring.

Even in pitch blackness, fish will change course when they are headed for a rock or obstacle. How are they warned? This mystery apparently is solved beyond question.

You may have noticed that fish have a line running down each side of their bodies. All along this line are tiny—in fact microscopic—organs that record changes in water pressure. When a fish swims toward a rock the pressure of water increases and the fish, warned, turns aside.

The frogs, toads and other amphibians appear to be still more alert and wary than the fish. A green frog mastered a maze with two blind alleys after a few dozen trials. More impressive, frogs and toads have been able to find their way home even though many obstacles (and other inviting pools) had to be passed.

The psychological standing of any animal is measured by its alertness and by its ability to adapt itself to strange conditions. In this respect reptiles are unmistakably superior to fish and frogs.

Only reptiles, for example, seem to be capable of actively hunting their prey. The alligator lies in wait for prey by the river bank, whereas fish don't seem to possess the cleverness to lie and wait for food.

Likewise the lizard (another reptile) often shows ingenuity and considerable adaptability in stalking prey. In the tropics lizards have been observed following a swarm of army ants. They stay behind, out of reach of the ants' bites and stings, but when ants drive an object of prey, such as a grasshopper, from cover, the lizard will leap in, grab the prize and dart off. It's all done in a flash.

And now we come to the birds, amazing creatures in many ways. They can appear to be both incredibly ingenious and incredibly dim-witted.

HOARDER

Uneasy about being watched, this crow hides his money. If a coin were stolen while he was away, he would miss it on his return.

Birds have remarkably keen eyesight and can easily learn to distinguish different form patterns. Chicks, for example, learned to discriminate between squares, circles and triangles much more successfully than the laboratory rat, a mammal. Other chicks were trained to distinguish between different shades of gray. One investigator suggests that "the visual organization of the bird is similar to that of man."

But more remarkable, birds can really count. In fact they can apparently count as well or better than certain primitive humans such as the Hottentots, who have great difficulty counting up to five.

In one test hens were trained to eat every third grain of corn out of a row of grain. At first the intervening two grains were glued down. But later even when they were left loose the hen still would only pick up every third one. If you think that is easy, try teaching a young child that he can have only every third lollipop in a box of lollipops!

Munro Fox, the distinguished British zoologist, reported a test in which birds were offered pieces of grain, one at a time. Ravens and parrots, for example, would pick up the first six grains offered, but shun the seventh because they knew it would be glued down. That was pretty clear evidence that they could count to seven.

In an even more difficult counting problem pigeons were taught to pick up five grains of corn, no more, no less. When that was learned, three grains were laid out

SAFETY FIRST

To insure against theft, the crow puts his money into safekeeping.

in front of a pile of wheat. A pigeon promptly picked up the three grains, then went to the pile and picked up two more, to bring the total up to five!

On the maze test, however, most of the birds that have been tested seem quite stupid. A chick did not do as well as a fish. And pigeons required 60 trials before they could get low scores on a six-alley maze that ants have mastered with ease.

Likewise birds aren't very impressive in puzzle boxes. They gradually learn to associate the process of stepping on a taut string with getting food but it is doubtful that they have any "idea" of the mechanics involved.

One chick that was dropped into a puzzle box for the first time whirled its head around to peck at its feathers to clean them. Accidentally its head hit the latch string and the door flew open. After that whenever the chick was tested it would whirl its head around and poke at its feathers just as soon as it was dropped in the box!

Here are some other bits of evidence which suggest that the bird's intelligence is extremely slight in certain situations.

A neighbor of the author saw a flicker fly up to a window of his home. When the flicker saw a reflection of itself in the windowpane it began pecking furiously at the windowpane, and did not stop until the blind was raised to remove the reflection.

All the evidence indicates that birds have extremely short memories when it comes to recognizing another bird. The memory of a specific individual can be retained only six or seven days at most. And adult birds can't remember even that long. Young birds remember

WHO'S THAT SILLY-LOOKING DUCK?

Her first glimpse of herself in a looking glass perplexed, rather than pleased, this duck. Many birds have been known to attack their own images in mirrors, apparently learning little from their repeated attempts to destroy their reflections.

their parents longer than parents remember their chicks.

When a gull chick became lost and later tried to return to the brood, the mother brained it and then ate the chick, apparently because it did not recognize its offspring in an odd situation.

Penguins spend much of their lives snatching fish out of the water. Fish is their sole diet. Yet when they come upon a fish lying on the ground they do not recognize it as food.

The penguin is a very "human," dignified-looking creature in an evening suit and appears to be very wise and knowing. Actually, while it is a fascinating creature it is also pretty stupid in some ways. It is a close relative of the wingless ostrich and kiwi, both of which are relative morons.

Thousands of years ago during the last Ice Age conditions became more and more harsh in the Antarctic. All birds and land animals escaped or perished except one—the penguin. It was trapped because it could not fly and it could not swim very far.

Survival has been a constant struggle. One result of this struggle—and one factor in the penguin's survival—is that penguin mothers feel a terrific, passionate love for their young and fight to the death for them. Psychologists as the Bronx Zoo found penguin mothers still mouth-feeding offspring that were two years old and practically full grown.

The penguins make their nests on the cold ice by piling up pebbles, which are the only materials available. Often the males have to carry these pebbles in their mouths for hundreds of yards. This stone-fetching is a major penguin occupation, and a major cause of trouble. Hauling stones is a nasty business and many lazy penguins take the obvious shortcut. They try to steal stones from a neighbor. Stone-stealing is the blackest crime possible in Penguindom, and those caught at it are set upon by the entire community.

One curious habit of the penguins is that frequently a whole crew of them will take off on a long hike, for no other apparent reason than that they enjoy sight-seeing.

Among birds as a whole, some appear to be clearly more intelligent than others. The chicken comes out very much better on maze tests than does the pigeon. Ross Baker, a Canadian psychologist who has trapped many birds for banding, reported:

"Cardinals are the canniest birds I've ever tried to trap. Once you have trapped them they will never fall into the same trap again. White-throated sparrows, on the other hand, are the stupidest birds I have encountered. They get caught over and over again."

One of the great mysteries about birds has been how they know when to migrate, particularly to fly north in the spring. Do they observe the appearance of leaves, or what?

The mystery was pretty definitely solved by an experiment conducted in Alberta, Canada. A large number of birds were captured at the time they normally move southward, around September 1, and held for two months. One group of the birds was allowed to receive diminishing amounts of daylight. The other group was given five minutes *more* daylight each day, by artificial illumination.

The sex organs of birds in this last group swelled in size day by day as the radiation increased. When, on November 9, those birds were released they flew straight north toward the Arctic! On the other hand, the sex organs of the birds that had gotten the normal, diminishing daylight had become much smaller, and when these birds were released they just wanted to stay near their warm nests.

We see in that experiment that Nature automatically

signals birds when it is time to migrate. They don't figure it out themselves.

Nature must also tell a mother bird when her young
are old enough to fly. At any rate it is an awe-inspiring
sight to see a litter of young wrens being pushed out
into the world. I witnessed this spectacle near my house.
A mother wren was nudging her five young wrens—one
at a time—out of the wren house. With her head the
mother would push a young sprout of a wren off the
limb out into the empty air.

Each young bird flew a bit awkwardly but adequately
right from the start. The mother would swoop ahead
and land on another branch. Then she would fly to a
higher branch with the youngster fluttering behind.
Thus up and up the tree she led each of the five wrens.

Nest-building by birds is a fine example of instinct in
action. We like to think, when we see an oriole building
its magnificent architectural structure, that it is showing
great individual ingenuity. Actually the oriole does not
yet know why it is building the nest.

Furthermore, the oriole probably did not begin assembling material for the nest until after it had mated.
It may have toyed with the milkweed fibers and long
moss it prefers for its nest, but it did not get the signal
from sex hormones in its blood to begin nest-building
until mating season began.

You will also notice, if you follow the oriole's movements from the start, that even after mating it will first
pick up materials and drop them about haphazardly,
before it starts assembling them in one spot. And it will
start several nests before the increasingly imperative sig-
naling of its hormones sets it seriously to work.

All of this, the psychologists say, is Nature in action,
not individual intelligence. Birds are capable of extremely complex behavior, but the behavior is invariably highly stereotyped. When birds are faced with a
problem requiring original thought (as when the hens

are separated from food by a short stretch of chicken wire) they make fools of themselves. This is understandable, for the bird does not have a well-developed cortex in its brain. And such a cortex, scientists believe, is a prerequisite for reasoning. Yale's Frank Beach summed it up this way:

"Birds have shown practically no indication of being able to solve problems in any way·except by simple learning. Even the fabled crow turns out to be incapable of passing a reasoning test."

There is a question whether birds (or reptiles, frogs, fish and insects) can even feel pain. Surely they can not feel pain if they are not conscious. And among scientists there is a reasonable doubt that consciousness exists among the lower animals we've been discussing. Munro Fox says in his *The Personality of Animals:*

"Among the different sorts of animals it is only mammals that have brains with a structure allowing us to assume that they may have consciousness. . . . If this anatomical argument is sound then birds can hardly be conscious, or only dimly so. For in the brain of birds that part which is the seat of our consciousness is hardly developed. For the same reason still less could reptiles or fish have consciousness. As for insects their brain is constructed on such totally different lines that it allows of no assumption on this score."

The fact that a worm may wiggle when you cut it in two does not necessarily mean it is in pain. The wiggling may be a reflex action. If laboratory scientists can ever clearly prove that the lower animals and some of the smaller mammals cannot feel pain, the scientists probably will be harassed less, in conducting their experiments on animals, by anti-vivisectionists and societies for the prevention of cruelty to animals. However, this theory is still not positively proven, and until it is, the opinion that Heywood Broun once offered has validity. He said:

"Fishermen and scientists are always telling me that a fish doesn't mind getting hooked; that it doesn't suffer. Well, I don't know. I think I'd like to get an opinion on the subject from a fish."

Whatever the answer is on pain, there is little question that all these lower animals we have been considering live extremely rigid stereotyped lives based overwhelmingly on instinct. They can learn to make simple modifications in specific situations, but once a modification is learned, conditions must be kept constant. The lowly ant can learn a complex maze, but if you change the maze in the slightest, once the maze is learned, the ant must start the learning process all over again.

None of these birds, reptiles, amphibians or insects could conceivably perform a feat of adaptability comparable to that of a black and white laboratory rat described in the *Journal of Genetic Psychology*.

The journal ran a series of photographs showing how this ingenious rat solved a problem that bothered him. The rat's private shelter was separated from a hot, exposed area where it had to eat its meals by a foot-high plank. Its meal was always served in a small bowl.

The rodent was obviously annoyed that it had to eat in a hot, exposed place and it began trying to find some way to get the bowl of food over the plank into its shelter.

Finally it moved the bowl over to the base of the plank. Then, climbing up on the plank, it curled its hind feet and tail over the top of the plank and stretched down as far as it could and just managed to get its teeth around the rim of the bowl. Slowly it backed up over the plank and deposited the bowl on the other side, without spilling a morsel of food!

That is a sample of the high-order ingenuity and adaptability we can expect of some mammals. So to the mammals we now turn.

5. Wizards and Numskulls of the Woodlands

IN the woodlands of North America there are two fascinating, furry animals that have much in common. I'm speaking of the 'possum and the coon. Both gather their food by night. Both spend most of their life in trees. Both have a prominent place in American folklore. In fact, they have so many superficial resemblances that the average American has trouble distinguishing one from the other.

Yet one of these two animals is just about the stupidest, dimmest-witted animal in the woods. And the other is a sheer genius whose wizardry in solving IQ tests has left psychologists gasping.

Can you guess which is which?

In our folklore the 'possum has a reputation for ingenuity. We use the expression "playing 'possum" to connote cunning deception. Every schoolchild knows that the 'possum feigns death when in danger.

The fact is, however, that the 'possum's reputation is undeserved. He is the dim-wit of the pair. It is now believed that his numb states when in danger are not *feints* but *faints*. He is too dumb to be an actor.

In a sense the opossum is a living fossil. He is the only surviving marsupial in North America, and in fact the only remaining marsupial left outside the continent of Australia.

A marsupial is, as you probably know, a mammal that

still carries its young in a pouch. It is a relic of a very ancient order of animal life that came on the earth when the Great Maker was experimenting with His first models of mammal life.

The outdated marsupials such as the kangaroo could survive in Australia only because for hundreds of thousands of years that continent has been isolated by water from the Asiatic mainland.

How the inefficient, disorderly-looking opossum with its small brain in a long, pointed skull has survived in America is an intriguing question. It lives in a sort of placid, sluggish trance and has no defense whatever to offer to its many fierce, relentless enemies that include the wildcat, the fox and the giant owl.

Apparently one factor that has helped it survive is that it is omnivorous. That is, it can eat almost anything—nuts, eggs, berries, bugs, cabbage.

But the major reason for its survival, naturalists believe, is that its females are fantastically fecund in bringing infants into the world. 'Possums make up for their ineptness by deluging the woods with new 'possum babies. One mother 'possum may produce three litters containing a total of 30 to 35 offspring in a single year!

Although an adult opossum is as large as a big tomcat, the 'possum's newborn babies are tiny blobs no bigger than your little finger. They are really still blind embryos barely able to wiggle. Yet somehow—in a way that only Nature knows—when born, after a gestation of only a couple of weeks, they wiggle their way along the mother's furry belly, crawl into the warm pouch and fasten their tiny mouths over one of their mother's teats. For the next six or seven weeks they suckle almost constantly inside the pouch's darkness.

When they emerge they are still not able to make their way in the world, but cling to their mother's furry back or tail as she goes in search of food. In many cases the mother will have a new litter in her pouch while an older litter is still riding her back. Thus at one time she may be carrying as many as 15 or 18 passengers!

A baby opossum's genes tell it how it is supposed to ride when its mother takes a trip. The baby opossums wind their tails securely around the mother's big tail. Then the mother opossum lifts her tail and arches it over her back so that all her little babies hang upside down over her back like inverted subway strap-hangers. In that position they accompany her safely on the journey.

Perhaps still another factor that has helped the 'possum survive is that it *does* go into a trance when faced with danger. When an enemy approaches the gentle 'possum almost literally becomes scared stiff. He apparently suffers a blackout of consciousness. His death-like stillness in this shock-produced trance sometimes saves his life. The great naturalist John Burroughs said that a 'possum is not himself wise but "Nature has been wise for him."

Now let us look at the self-made genius of the pair—the raccoon, one of the great animal personalities of North America.

The raccoon appears to be very clumsy as it backs its stout body down a tree trunk. But don't let appearances deceive you. Indians, who know more about animals then do most naturalists, have always had the profoundest respect for the coon's cunning, adroitness and subtlety. The Bureau of American Ethnology collects Indian folk stories and has observed that a very large proportion of them deal with the wizardry of the coon, which the Indians called "The Black-masked Little Bear."

Our greatest pioneers and naturalists such as Daniel Boone, Davy Crockett and John James Audubon all wore coonskin caps. Yet today the coon is still surviving very nicely in modern, atomic-age America. It is so re-

sourceful that it often prowls right into the suburbs of our largest cities.

In the psychologist's laboratory the coon is a riot. He will put his paws into the psychologist's pocket just to see what is there and he will go back into puzzle boxes after he has opened them just for the fun of operating the gadgets.

Most of the standard puzzle boxes, such as those that baffle a dog, are child's play to a coon. One psychologist, in a supreme burst of ingenuity, invented a box from which the coon could get out only by operating seven different devices. The coon had to depress two different pedals . . . pull down on a loop of string . . . lift a latch . . . slide back a bolt . . . undo a hook . . . and press down on a thumb latch.

Before long the coon was getting out of this Houdini contraption in eight seconds flat!

Recently a curator of the American Museum of Natural History reported on his problem in coping with coons at the museum's camp for youngsters at the Bear Mountain State Park in New York. One night the camp was thrown into pandemonium by a howling girl. She had been awakened by a bushy, ringed tail brushing her face. An old coon had climbed across her bed and was trying to reach under the girl's mattress for some chocolate she had hidden there.

The curator tried to keep several coons in cages for the children to watch but found it difficult because of "the vast number of escapes from our cages." Some of the coons, he said, appear to escape just for the fun of it, then stick around after they have shown off and allow themselves to be put back into the cages without protest.

BRIGHT-EYES IS ALSO A BRIGHT BOY

The nimble-witted raccoon wouldn't think of eating his food before he had scrubbed it vigorously in water. He can also use his forepaws with amazing dexterity to operate psychologists' puzzle boxes, which are child's play to his keen intelligence.

DON'T GET ANY CLOSER

One of the most well-protected of all woodland animals is the porcupine. Those long needles of his, combined with a sharp intelligence, make him a dangerous foe to attack.

One coon was very congenial and playful with everyone on the staff—except one man. For some reason unknown to that man the coon had a grudge against him and would lunge at him in fury. Apparently he just took a dislike to the guy's looks.

Curiosity is an index of intelligence, but the coon is so curious that it often lands him in trouble. Trappers have learned to play on the curiosity of the coon. They have found the coon much too smart to fall for the standard animal traps. The wise trappers decorate their coon traps with all sorts of outlandish, glittering trimmings such as Christmas tree decorations.

Other animals also have apparently become wise to the coon's incredible curiosity. In one outdoor laboratory where a psychologist had a coon and a badger, the coon made life miserable for the badger. Whenever the badger tried to nap under its favorite alder tree, the coon would playfully prod the badger in the rear, being careful to keep himself out of range of the badger's powerful jaws. He kept the badger awake and reduced it to despair.

One afternoon the harassed badger yawned as if in sleepy boredom but kept his mouth wide open as if he had contracted lockjaw. For several minutes he sat with his mouth gaping like an idiot. This perplexed the curious coon. The coon began edging closer and closer to see what on earth was the matter. Finally he peered inside the mouth.

The badger's jaws flashed shut! When the howling coon finally pulled himself loose his curious nose was half ripped off. After that whenever the coon went near the badger's kennel he involuntarily put his paw over his nose.

There have been many similar reports of the coon's impishness. One investigator tells of the coon that pulled feathers from the tails of passing roosters and tried to stick them in his own head. The same man also tells of the caged coon that would pile up a number of small stones and carefully await a chance to fling them into a flock of young chickens. If you passed him by without paying your respects to him he would growl and whine.

Another investigator reported that one of his coons would playfully tip over the water basin as soon as it was filled, right before the attendant's eyes.

The main factor that has given the coon a reputation for ingenuity (aside from the fact that it has a nimble mind) is its extraordinary dexterity in the use of its forepaws. A coon can easily snatch a bee out of the air with its paw. If you think that is easy, try doing it with your own vastly bigger hand!

One food the raccoon adores is ripening sweet corn. He is able to strip its husk away with his forepaws. The coon can also pick up extremely minute morsels of food with its paw and insert the food in its mouth.

When a coon begins to eat a piece of food, whether it be a crayfish or a snail, he will wash it thoroughly by dipping it into water and scrubbing it with his paws. This is instinctive and apparently is more of a dunking than a washing operation. When the coon has nothing else to do, he will wash pebbles and lay them out to dry.

Coons are also regarded by some naturalists as reliable weather prophets. Farmers believe that if a coon's fur is long it means a hard winter; if short, a mild winter. One naturalist relates:

"One day in September 1938 I saw a clan of raccoons gathered in a circle in the middle of a country road and they all acted very nervous. I knew something was afoot. But I didn't know that the great hurricane of 1938 would break the next day."

Another American woodland animal that has an almost legendary reputation for ingenuity is the busy beaver. Here, however, a somewhat different kind of wisdom is involved.

The beaver builds dams, and moated homes inside the dams, that are monuments of architectural ingenuity. Dams have been discovered in the Rockies that were nearly a quarter of a mile long. They had been built higher and wider by each beaver generation.

In building their dams, beavers have felled trees more than a yard in diameter. Typically, however, they prefer the smaller aspens and birches. In one night a typical beaver can cut down a tree six inches in diameter, cut it into six-foot lengths, and haul the lengths to the water.

The beavers begin their dams by hauling young saplings to the dam site, placing the thick butt ends upstream facing the current, and laying rocks and mud on the bushy ends. They add hundreds of tons of material until they have raised the water level several feet. With the dam completed they pile up rocks and mud at a spot in the middle of the water to build a small island. And on that island they build a domed mud and stick home with a small hole left in the top for ventilation.

In these island fortresses the beavers are absolutely protected from all marauders. Their domed homes often are 35 feet wide at the base.

Human engineers surveying mountain areas for the best possible dam sites have often found—after studying topographical maps and all other information available—that the best possible site turns out to be a place where beavers have already built a dam.

Beavers love to work, cut down trees even when they do not need them, and are constantly puttering around their dams.

The beaver is a rodent related fairly closely to the squirrel. Its wisdom, investigators have decided, is not the versatile ingenuity of the coon but rather is largely the instinctive routinized kind implanted by Nature in the species. Zoologists state that the beaver's instinctive feats are the most complex performed by any animal in nature, vastly more complex than the feats of the oriole or the army ants.

More advanced types of individual intelligence and adaptability are shown in the tricks the fox and wolf use to lure victims or escape pursuers. Foxes have been observed putting fishheads out in conspicuous open places apparently as bait for hawks because they would lie in wait for the hawks to appear. Occasionally also a fox that is being pursued by human hunters has reportedly plunged into the water and remained almost entirely immersed to escape the hunters.

Wolves regularly hunt cooperatively and have been seen organizing an ambush for antelope. In one reported instance a part of the pack chased an antelope right up to the waiting jaws of companions in hiding.

If you ask a Canadian trapper to name the most ingenious animal in the North Woods he will answer: the wolverine—and then probably utter a volley of curses.

Trappers know the wolverine as "The Devil" or "Devil of the Woods." Whenever they hear of a wolverine in their vicinity they are filled with foreboding and despair, because the animal is an accomplished wrecker and thief.

Although the wolverine is only as large as a bulldog, it kills deer and is feared by every animal in the forest because of its fantastic strength, its ferocity, its cunning, and utter fearlessness. Even mountain lions and grizzly bears avoid it. Most animals have some sense of ownership but the Devil considers everything in sight as fair game and steals from other animals and from Man.

A trapper in the North Woods must have in or near his cabin large food caches to see him through the winter. These are not safe from raids by the wolverine while the trapper is making the rounds of his traps. And his traps are at the mercy of raids by the wolverine while he is at camp.

An experienced old wolverine will follow the trapper on his rounds and steal the bait from every single trap without springing the traps himself. If he gets his toes nipped by a trap he will bury the trap or throw it into the river in a fit of fury.

In tackling an empty cabin containing food, the wolverine tries doors and windows, crawls down the chimney, burrows underneath walls or hides in wait for the careless minute when the trapper will leave the door ajar. Once inside, the wolverine gorges himself, then destroys everything he can't lug off.

An expert for the Field Museum of Natural History reports the case of a wolverine that worked night and day for almost a week to get to a cache of food protected by an enormous pile of logs. The relentless wolverine chewed through logs a foot thick and dragged away logs ten times his own weight.

HE'S A SMART ONE, ALL RIGHT

But he's not as intelligent as the wolverine or the raccoon. In fact, the fox's entire psychology is geared for flight rather than pursuit. As a result, he's inclined to become emotional in a situation that would cause the wolverine to start thinking logically.

The wolverine is the biggest member of the weasel family, which contains the most deadly, highly skilled hunters in the entire animal kingdom. The family also includes, for example, the fisher, the marten and the otter.

Weasels themselves are ferocious little creatures, utterly without fear, whose jaws lock when they bite into a rabbit or chicken. They quietly seize the blood vein of the neck of a fowl and kill their victim before it can warn others in the flock.

The fishermen of the weasel family are the otters, who share the fearlessness of other weasels but are more frolicsome than ferocious. They can swim faster than a canoeist can paddle and are a delight to watch as they twist and turn in the water. Sea otters are somewhat chunkier than the regular otters of woodland streams.

A scientist studying a school of sea otters near Carmel, California, reported a remarkable incident to the *Journal of Mammalogy*. The sea otters were lying on their backs in the water and holding a flat stone across their chests. When the otters dove for shellfish they would bring up with each shellfish a flat stone. As they reached the surface, they would roll over on their backs, balance the stone on their chests and use the stone as an anvil upon which they cracked the shellfish's armor!

HIS SKIN IS
HIS WORST ENEMY

Relentlessly pursued by Man because of his valuable fur, the otter is a harmless, fun-loving aquatic animal, who possesses much native wisdom. A highly skilled hunter, he is a playful fellow in his leisure moments. One of his most amusing games is to make mud slides, down which he plummets like a five-year-old on a playground.

6. Giants with Big and Little Brains

JUST as the woodlands have, in the coon and 'possum, two extremes in wisdom, the jungles of Africa and Asia have a pair of goliaths that offer startling contrasts in the matter of wits.

Both the elephant and the rhinoceros are behemoths which children at the zoo tend to lump into the same class. But whereas the elephant has a good-sized brain mass in relation to its huge body and with the mass a relatively brilliant mind, the rhino, although it weighs two tons and is often 14 feet long, doesn't have the brains of a mouse.

An Iowa State Teachers' College biologist who made a study of the rhinoceros concluded that it is "Nature's prize numskull."

Old Hooklip, as the rhino is affectionately known, is a misfit, a biological has-been that has somehow managed to survive. The hook on its lip marks it as being behind the times, the product of an early experiment by Nature during the evolution of mammals.

All other self-respecting mammals that have horns have the horns where they can be used effectively in combat. The poor old rhino still has his hook on his upper lip where it doesn't do much good because he can't put his full weight behind it. The hook is two feet long in some cases. The Indian rhinoceros has one hook, the African rhino still has two.

Practically all big game hunters agree that Old Hooklip, for all his ferocious appearance, puts up a sad excuse for a fight. While he has a vicious temper, he is not nearly as dangerous to hunt as the water buffalo, the elephant or the lion.

Carl Akeley, the great naturalist and hunter, became convinced that the rhino is no longer dangerous if he misses you on the first lunge. A water buffalo will turn swiftly and charge back at you but the rhino has such a dim mind that the chances are that by the time he gets past you he has forgotten what he started out to do!

While the rhino is dumb, he is not modest about it. The slightest disturbance, a snapping twig or a fluttering bird, will set him rampaging through the jungle. He has such bad eyesight that he can't tell for sure what caused the disturbance, but he intends to show the world he's not scared. His irritability may also be due to the fact that swarms of blood-sucking parasites live on his back and may drain more than a gallon of blood from his system in a day.

Old Hooklip's diet befits his modest mind. He eats mainly thorns and bitter herbs. The rhino's problem in surviving in the modern world has been aggravated by the fact that the Chinese consider Old Hooklip's hook to be mighty powerful medicine. The hook is sold to the Chinese for half its weight in gold. Even his blood is considered good medicine and sells, in dried form, for a dollar a pound.

In contrast to Old Hooklip, the bad-tempered moron, the elephant has a jumbo-sized mind. Psychologists who have made a study of elephantine mentality are developing a deep respect for it. The evidence is still in-

WORLD'S PRIZE NUMSKULL

Old Hooklip, the rhinoceros, is bad-tempered, slovenly, and a Grade-A moron. About the most that can be said for him is that his diet fits his modest mentality: he thrives on thorns and bitter herbs.

complete, but what is available is flattering to the elephant. Dr. Riess, for example, told me: "I suspect that the elephant will prove to rate pretty high."

The elephants tested at the Bronx Zoo caught on very rapidly to the idea of pulling strings to get hidden food in the shell game test. And in the teakwood jungles of southeast Asia investigators are finding that elephants casually perform tasks requiring a high order of brainwork, much higher, for example, than the work expected of a farm horse. And these elephants do it without much supervision from Man. In practically all instances elephants readily learn the tasks assigned to them.

They stack huge teakwood logs neatly into piles. And they give every sign of comprehending a mechanical principle, which is extraordinary for animals below the primates. One mechanical principle they seem to understand is the log slide. They place logs on the slide, maneuver them carefully into position with their trunks,

then give them a push with their forefeet—and watch critically while the log swooshes down into the water.

Each elephant had to learn this mechanical operation individually. It could not be instinct, because in its natural habitat it has never had to stack logs.

In talking about elephants it is important to distinguish between Asiatic and African elephants. Practically all the elephants you see in circuses and in zoos are of the Asiatic variety, not only because they are easier to obtain but because they are more friendly and tractable. African elephants are terribly hard to tame. They don't do nearly as well in IQ tests and in other man-made tests, but that may be because they are so wild and unmanageable.

The African elephant at the Bronx Zoo proved to be an unimpressive scholar. She acted very frightened, and instead of pulling the string, would walk away. To the

Asiatic elephants, string pulling was no problem at all.

One easy way to tell whether the elephant you are looking at is Asiatic or African is to look at its ears. The Asiatic elephant's ears are small and tend to look like the map of India. In contrast, the African elephant has enormous floppy ears that hang halfway to the ground. The African elephant is usually taller, but the Asiatic elephant is bulkier.

A swaying six-ton elephant at first glance looks hopelessly clumsy and handicapped by its enormous bulk. Actually the elephant is fantastically adroit and precise in picking up things it wants by manipulating its trunk. One evidence of this dexterity is the fact that in the IQ tests, elephants were able to pick up and pull a string lying on a board.

The trunk of the elephant is one of Nature's really original and ingenious creations. Most people think the trunk is a big tube through which the elephant sucks water and food. Actually the trunk is a sort of combination hand, arm, antenna and suction pump. An elephant does not eat with its trunk, but uses it rather to pick up food it wishes to stuff into its mouth, and uses it to suck water to squirt down its throat.

The trunk is made up of the upper lip and nose. There are two lips on the end of its trunk and they are almost as useful as our fingers.

If you watch an elephant at a zoo, you will see it sweep out its trunk in a deft movement and pick up a single piece of popcorn. Occasionally it will stick its trunk into a neighboring elephant's mouth to feel what

JUMBO-SIZED—IN MIND AND BODY

The elephant has a subtle, wily, adaptable mind. Here you see one standing on its head, something which no other animal can be taught. It can reason independently and does not depend on memory. In fact, the expression "an elephant never forgets" is sheer folklore. The elephant really has a very bad memory, as any elephant-trainer will tell you.

the neighbor is eating. One female elephant was seen reaching into a boy's pocket for a lump of sugar it knew was there. . . . In addition to using its trunk in feeding, the elephant employs the trunk to break off branches of trees, to test uncertain ground and to sniff the air for the scent of an enemy.

Reports on the behavior of elephants at circuses likewise uniformly indicate that Jumbo has a subtle, wily, adaptable mind. One investigator concluded that Jumbo has to take a back seat only to chimpanzees and orangutans when it comes to learning circus stunts. The investigator stated:

"The elephant is smart and adaptable. However, anything you teach an elephant must be done before he is ten."

That age ceiling, when you think of it, is not too insulting to the elephant. We have the saying that "You can't teach an old dog new tricks," which applies to a surprising degree to human beings as well as to animals. Johnson O'Connor, the engineer who has made exhaustive studies of human learning, has found that the average person's vocabulary virtually stops growing after the age of 25.

An elephant can be trained to stand on its head. How many other animals—including the dog—are there that could match that balancing feat?

Many centuries ago Plutarch spoke of a trained elephant that often, in the privacy of its own yard, was seen practicing her steps when nobody was watching.

An elephant at the Ringling Brothers circus became nervous about a tub that she was supposed to sit on. The tub had a tendency to wobble under her weight, and during one performance she fell off the tub in front of everybody and obviously was deeply mortified. During several succeeding performances she would keep her beady eyes fixed on that treacherous tub and would squat on it with the greatest reluctance. Finally she resumed her placid behavior during the performance and the trainer was greatly relieved.

It was not until several weeks later that someone noticed that she wasn't actually sitting on the tub at all! She would assume the squatting position and lower her posterior down to within a fraction of an inch of the tub, then during the performance hold her six-ton body in suspension.

That is an example of an animal solving an original problem by a mental process very close to reasoning.

There have also been reports of circus elephants showing unusual presence of mind. During a performance the elephants were walking around the ring, led by an old elephant named Big John. John's headgear, during a head-standing stunt, had slipped down over his eyes but he continued through the routine.

Suddenly serious trouble arose. One of the younger elephants in the line became frightened by an exotic hat which a lady near by in the audience was wearing, and began bellowing and whirling. Other elephants joined excitedly in the milling. There was dangerous pandemonium.

Big John felt his way to a post, pushed the headgear that was blinding him away from his eyes. Then he whirled and began trumpeting orders in a very firm voice. He lashed the milling young elephants with his trunk, and soon had them subdued and back in line.

In the jungle there have been unverified reports of elephants carrying palm trees in their trunks to shade themselves from the sun on hot days.

The average elephant eats about 150 pounds of food a day and drinks 50 gallons of water. Usually elephants have an agreeable disposition but this amiability cannot be relied upon. The males are subject to periodic outbursts of violent rage (which is why most elephants in zoos and circuses are females) and all elephants become cranky—just as we do—if they have a toothache.

In the jungle of Uganda an enraged elephant felled a native with his trunk, gored him with his tusks, tramped on him with his feet, then with his trunk flung the man more than 75 feet away.

Natives in the Congo rarely try to kill an elephant by hunting. It is too dangerous. Instead they set lethal traps for the elephant. They search out a well-used elephant trail, find two large trees straddling the trail, then suspend huge logs 50 feet in the air over the trail. The logs are triggered by a vine stretched across the trail. Fastened to the ends of the logs are sharp iron spearheads. Woe to the man that trips over one of those traps in the dark!

Elephants are reputed to have extraordinary memories, but here apparently the elephant has been overrated by our folklore. It has been established that they do not have as good memories as monkeys. Circus trainers find that an elephant will forget its routine from one season to the next if it is not rehearsed frequently.

Baby elephants have been seen sucking the tail and trunk of its mother rather than the teats. That at first glance would look like stupidity. Actually, it is one more evidence that elephants have a high capability for learning. Only among the lower animals with small IQs do we find infant animals that show much wisdom. Their wisdom is instinctive, written into their genes.

It is almost a rule of animal behavior that the more clumsy and awkward an infant is at birth, the more likely it is to show intelligent adaptability as it grows up. Its instincts are imperfectly developed to permit it to learn by trial and error how to take care of itself.

The supreme example of an awkward, clumsy infant is the human baby, which is utterly helpless for the first six months of its life. It will suck any nipple-like object within reach, including its own thumb. The baby elephant's sucking behavior is no more outlandish.

7. How Wise Are Man's Best Friends?

I F you ask the average person what the smartest animal in the world is, you'll probably get one of three answers: the dog, the horse, or the cat.

In America there are 20 million dogs, 10 million cats and there are still a few million horses. Most of these have a human owner; and most of the millions of human owners tend to develop a deep sentimental affection for their four-legged friends. They proudly recount the clever feats of their Fido, Dobbin or Muff. And they go to the movies to see a collie leaping up through a transom to rescue his master, or to see a cow horse push villains onto the waiting fists of the Western hero. As a result of all this we tend to think of dogs, horses and cats as in a class apart from "dumb animals."

How smart are these dumb animals, actually? A great deal of authoritative evidence is now at hand. Let's take up one animal at a time. First, the dog.

I have a dog named Dixie and believe I qualify as a "dog-lover." The dog, in my opinion, is the most lovable animal in the world. My Dixie, certainly, is a superb and loyal companion. Yet some months ago I was branded a dog-hater. I had written an article about animals for *The American Magazine* (later reprinted in *The Reader's Digest*) in which I tried to present objectively a few of the psychologists' findings concerning canine intelligence. Hundreds of readers wrote me

EXCEPTION TO THE RULE

Sheep dogs and collies are among the most intelligent members of the dog world. In most cases, Man's best friend is loyal but slow. The collie in this picture has learned to get to the top of the ladder, but it took hours of painstaking repetition to teach him.

abusive letters. A mild example is the letter I got from a veterinary student at Michigan State College. He wrote:

"Your stupid and groundless maligning of the dog irritated me beyond all bounds."

Since writing that article I spent a good many hours digging up further information on canine behavior. I had even spent an hour observing a dog named Tubby who had been hailed as the most remarkable dog in America. Here I will try to summarize my findings.

Some dogs, it appears, are considerably more intelligent than others. And the typical dog is a friendly, devoted, amusing, and spirited companion to any human master who has a congenial disposition. He is truly Man's best friend. But right at the start I might as well set down one fact. I still have not found any psychologist investigating the mental powers of dogs who has a particularly high opinion of canine intelligence.

Yale's Professor Beach, for example, has stated that the only problems which the dog "can solve without previous practice are so elementary that the behavior scarce-

NOTHING SPECTACULAR

This collie, for a dog, is pretty bright. Yet, he can perform no feats that are higher than simple learning. He responds only to unconscious cues from his owner. Contrast this to the reasoning power of the chimpanzee, which can handle itself intelligently in any new situation.

ly qualifies as reasoning." Dr. Riess told me that dogs as a whole "don't rank very high—in fact they rank low" when it comes to figuring out new problems. C. J. Warden, T. N. Jenkins and L. H. Warner in their massive, three-volume *Introduction to Comparative Psychology* state that the dog's intelligence has been vastly overrated.

When a dog faces a new problem he is apt to act like a dope. And it is not because he doesn't try. The dog will struggle for hours at a test if he is rewarded with an occasional pat. He is an ideal psychological subject. But stick-to-itiveness is not enough. In fact it can be a handicap. As Professor Beach says, "The ability to give up an unsuccessful line of attack and shift to a new one is fundamental to practical reasoning."

On the puzzle box, for example, the dog is a moron compared to the raccoon. A dog will paw and run around at random. If he opens the box, it is usually accidentally, at first. And although dogs will soon learn how to open simple puzzle boxes, they don't seem to comprehend the principle involved. They rarely seem to understand cause and effect, which understanding is the basis of higher intelligence.

In one test when several dogs had finally learned to open a box containing a bone, by pushing down a protruding lever, the psychologist gave the box a quarter turn. Thereupon the dogs were completely baffled. They ran to the box and made motions with their paws at the place where the lever *had been,* even though the lever was in plain sight a few inches away. Such behavior would make a chimpanzee snicker.

Only gradually did they learn to open the box in that new position. And when they did learn it, a second quarter-turn put them in a quandary all over again.

Many scientists who have given the "fence test" to the dog—by separating it from a bone by a stretch of wire which has a hole a few feet away—are convinced that the dog usually discovers the hole only by chance while clawing the fence and trotting excitedly back and forth.

Most dog-owners will swear that their dog can learn a trick by watching another dog perform it. Such imitation has never been achieved by dogs tested in an experimental laboratory.

In one test a dog was taught to jump onto a box at a given signal. After each jump it was rewarded with a piece of food. Then a second dog was brought in to watch. Although Dog 2 was pathetically eager to get the food it never caught the idea of jumping on the box to get it—even though Dog 1 performed the feat before its eyes 110 times.

There are many dog-owners who are also positive that their dog understands words that are spoken to it. In case you believe you have a dog that understands you, try this experiment.

Select some command which he normally obeys and which he seems to understand, such as "Rover, roll over!" But change your tone. For example, say it softly and casually. If the psychologists are right, Rover will stare at you. Or, better still, stick to your usual tone and gestures but use nonsense words such as "Blowbar, mole lobber!" Then, presumably, Rover will roll over, unless he happens to be an extraordinarily alert dog.

One of the many people who wrote to me to defend the braininess of dogs was a prominent New York executive, who stated:

"I have an old setter dog who can tell a Buick motor from a Cadillac by its sound. I know because when I come home in a Buick he appears, but Cadillacs can drive by the place all day and he pays no attention to them. Are your chimpanzees and orangutans that mechanical?"

Actually this is not being "mechanical" at all. Dogs

have a prodigious sense of hearing. Animal psychologists have found that a typical dog can hear the ticking of a watch that is 40 feet away. The sharpest-eared man can hear the watch at no more than four or five feet.

But hearing is not intelligence. The executive's dog—with its fine, discriminating ear—had learned to associate a particular motor sound with Master. Whenever it heard that sound it would leap to its feet and run out in a sort of conditioned reflex.

All dogs, of course, are domesticated wolves—even the little Pekingese. To produce the 111 different breeds of dogs that exist in America today Man had to breed for thousands of years. His first problem was to take the wild-wolf fire out of the dog and to breed for timidity, or at least for disciplined, obedient aggressiveness. Another early problem was to breed out of the wolf-dog its antagonism to Man and substitute in its place an attraction to Man, an eagerness to please Man, a trait that some animals could never learn. It would be utterly impossible, for example, to train a chicken or any other animal under the mammal to care a hoot about pleasing man.

When this was done, dogs were bred for specific desired traits. Terriers were selected for their alertness of ear and eye, while hounds were selected for their ability to stalk prey by scent.

Gradually, though breeding and being trained by Man, dogs began to take on many of the traits of their masters. The noted dog trainer, Blanche Saunders, for example, states:

"Over the centuries dogs took on characteristics of the races they lived with."

She points out that the Scottish terrier is a dour, solemn hard-working dog, as Scottish people tend to be, while the Kerry Blue (Irish) terrier is gay, unpredictable and loves to fight. This, she implies, is a trait of the Irish people, and points out that movie actor Mickey Rooney has a Kerry Blue.

"German dogs, in the same way, exhibit characteristics which are commonly regarded as typically German. They adore discipline to such an extent that if you fail to discipline them they will endeavor to discipline you. Boxers, Doberman pinschers, German shepherds and even little dachshunds will virtually click their heels in obedience for a firm master."

In the past dogs were bred to do specific helpful tasks: tending sheep, tracking game or hauling carts. Today the great majority of dogs are cherished primarily for companionship. In our cities and suburbs homes are so small that there is little room for a big dog, and many budgets can ill afford a hearty, wolfish eater. Thus the trend has been to small friendly dogs, such as Boston terriers, beagles, spaniels.

The use of German shepherds during World War I plus the great vogue of Rin Tin Tin of the movies brought a temporary fad for German shepherds during the twenties. For quite a while the collie, because of its big size, was losing popularity. Then a decade ago it rose from twelfth to third place on the canine hit parade—largely because of the movie popularity of a collie called Lassie.

Millions of young TV-watchers became convinced that Lassie was brilliant, and smarter than many people. So let's look at Lassie as she was at the height of her popularity.

The first thing we observe about Lassie is that she was not a "she" at all, but a he-dog. His name was Pal, but his first big role was to star in the children's classic about a she-dog, *Lassie Come Home*.

Lassie learned (by conventional training methods) to jump a hurdle, yawn, lie down, crawl, play dead, etc. It is significant that when he worked before a camera, this canine star always had to be facing his trainer and owner who stood or squatted just out of range of the camera and gave commands. Sometimes the trainer crawled under chairs, stuck his head through a transom or peeked through a hidden hole in the wall so that Lassie could always see his face.

When Lassie stretched up full length on a door, seemingly eager to get out, he was actually playing with his master who was on a catwalk above dangling Lassie's favorite plaything, a net rag. In the touching scenes where Lassie kissed the boy star he was actually licking ice cream from the boy's cheek. And when Lassie gazed adoringly at the movie heroine, he was actually gazing with great fascination at a dog biscuit his trainer was holding just beyond.

Collies, shepherds and other canines that for centuries received training as sheep dogs, however, are generally regarded as among the most intelligent of all dogs. It requires a high degree of alertness and versatility to go out into a field, round up a flock, retrieve strays, bring in the entire flock and then cut out a marked sheep, which is what a skilled sheep dog can do.

The sheep dog even shows some indication of being able to learn through something close to *imitation,* which is apparently impossible for most dogs. When a young sheep dog learns to drive sheep by accompanying an experienced dog, it may learn partly by imitation. But probably it is more accurate to say that it learns by *participation.*

For some time the smartest dog known to experimental psychology was a German shepherd named Fellow who had learned to respond to a hundred commands, and could work steadily on psychology for three hours at a stretch without any reward except to hear the displeased or approving comments voiced by his master.

Several years ago a new star appeared on the horizon,

a dog named Tubby who belonged to a friendly, earnest Wellsboro, Pennsylvania, farmer. Tubby was not a pedigreed dog. He was three-fourths collie and his owner suspected the other fourth was either shepherd or St. Bernard.

The owner stated that Tubby can do about 150 "things" including count and talk. Tubby herded cows, gathered firewood and carried messages out to his master in the fields. The Gaines Dog Research Center cited Tubby as "The Most Useful Animal in America."

Dr. J. B. Rhine, the famed Duke University psychologist, went to Wellsboro to watch Tubby in action and afterward stated that Tubby was one of the most intelligent dogs he had ever seen, and quite possibly was the most intelligent dog in the country.

While Tubby was visiting the Gaines Research Center I went to take a look at him. His master scattered 15 objects—such as wallet, pipe, chain, hat, handbag—on the floor about 25 feet from us. Then he commanded Tubby to go and fetch him various items. Later he repeated some of the objects to show that he was following no special order. Tubby performed very nicely on this test except that he became confused on the pipe command.

Next we turned to mathematics. His master held up a dollar bill and asked: how much? Tubby barked once. Then he held up a $5 bill and Tubby barked five times. When Tubby was asked how much "one plus four" equals he barked six times, then corrected it to five. Some psychologists contend that no dog can count without a cue. Tubby's master said: "I do have to use a cue on any sum of numbers over ten, below that Tubby just knows." Possibly his master, wholly unconsciously, gives a cue in the way he words his questions or looks at Tubby. This could best be determined by an investigation under controlled laboratory conditions.

Finally we came to talking. His master stated that

Tubby could answer "No" or "I don't know" or "I don't want to" to certain questions, but added that Tubby's "I" was a Southern "Ah." When Tubby talked to me he could have been talking or he could have been making guttural grunts. By using your imagination you could believe he said "I don't know." His master said Tubby was hot (it was a hot day) and was "not talking so plain."

In summary I would say that Tubby was a fascinating and unusually bright dog, but there was no valid evidence I could see that he could perform any feats that involved mental processes higher than simple learning.

While dogs may not be able to pass tests that call for reasoning or exercise of higher mental problems, they are capable of some very interesting behavior that certainly involves a high degree of mental alertness. I will conclude by mentioning two examples.

—First is an authenticated case involving association and memory. A lady with a cocker spaniel went to visit a woman in Darien, Connecticut, who owns an English setter. The two dogs had a wonderful time playing with a big, inflated red ball on the living-room floor. They got along so nicely that three weeks later the woman came to visit a second time with her dog. This time the English setter seemed to pay no attention to his guest but kept trying rudely to get out of the house. Finally the dog's mistress, exasperated, opened the door. The dog dashed around the house to the spot where the same red ball was lying under a tree, and began barking.

—Dr. Gustav Eckstein, the University of Cincinnati physiologist, has reported the case of a spitz dog that took care of a diabetic woman by sleeping in the crook of her arm every night. The woman occasionally sank into comas. Whenever her breathing changed at the beginning of a coma, the dog would rush into the next room and wake up the woman's daughter.

8. What Do You Mean—Horse Sense?

IN Oswego, New York, a milk-wagon horse stood patiently by the curb while its master was delivering milk. Suddenly the horse became alarmed and began rearing and whinnying. Apparently it had been startled by the noise made by a boy kicking a tin can along the sidewalk.

The horse began charging down the street with the milk-wagon careening wildly behind it. Too late, the milkman ran after the horse shouting. But the horse would not halt, not even for policemen who waved their night sticks at it. For a half mile the runaway horse raced. Then suddenly it came abruptly to a skidding halt.

Why did it stop? Because it had come to a red light!

A good many horse-lovers have cited this incident as one more proof of the horse's wisdom. Other people have cited this same incident to illustrate the force of conditioning on even a dumb, hysterical creature.

Just how wise is the horse anyhow? When people speak of "horse sense" they usually use the phrase admiringly. They are suggesting that the horse possesses great down-to-earth shrewdness, common sense and wisdom. Does it?

Scientists themselves have been arguing this question for at least 50 years. Scientific commissions have been formed to investigate the intelligence of horses that have performed apparently remarkable feats.

The first great equine to come under scientific scrutiny was Clever Hans, the most famous talking horse of all time.

Hans began astonishing the scientific world back at the turn of the century, when a man in Berlin, Herr von Osten, announced that he possessed a four-footed genius. His Hans, he announced, could not only count and subtract but could solve complicated mathematical problems and could "talk," in the sense that he understood, and could reply to questions which were presented to him either verbally or in writing (German).

The owner had suspected that Hans, behind his noble face, possessed great wisdom if it could only be communicated. He and Hans worked out the following system for communication.

Hans answered the mathematical problems by tapping on the floor with his front hoofs. He designated single units by tapping with his right foot, and designated units of ten with his left foot. Thus if an answer was 43 he would tap four times with his left foot, then three times with this right. Hans could even convert fractions into decimals.

In saying "Paris is the capital of France" Hans likewise would "talk" by tapping out each letter in a sort of Morse code arrangement. Each letter was spelled by a certain number of taps, indicated on an alphabet chart placed on a stand before Han's eyes.

Herr von Osten proudly exhibited his Hans to sightseers but, it should be stressed, he never charged admission or tried in any way to exploit Hans commercially.

The feats of Hans created so much excitement in Germany that a committee of respected scientists was formed to investigate him. Two German professors published monographs affirming that Hans was a truly brilliant animal. A zoologist stated publicly that there was no question that Hans was genuinely capable of high order reasoning.

Still there were skeptics. Investigations continued. Many investigators kept a hard, analytical eye on Herr von Osten during the performances. But for the life of them they could find no evidence that he was secretly giving Hans cues or that there was any other connivance between the master and Hans.

Finally a scientist suggested one slight variation in the routine of asking Hans questions—by writing them on a small blackboard which the master was to hold up. The scientist suggested that someone else should write the questions, and that the master should not be permitted to see the question written on the board.

When this was done, Han's brilliance seemed to evaporate. He couldn't even answer two plus two.

Herr von Osten was bewildered and humiliated. He protested that he had not been giving Hans cues, but he couldn't account for Han's sudden show of stupidity. When von Osten began again asking or writing the questions Han's brilliance returned. Eventually, after step-by-step analysis, the explanation became clear.

The master had not been cuing Hans *deliberately* but nonetheless there had been slight clues that the sharp-eyed Hans had responded to, to get his lump of sugar. As Hans began tapping, Herr von Osten would become tense and count silently with Hans. When Hans had tapped out the right answer, the master would relax slightly, and Hans—cued by the relaxed posture—would stop tapping! It was found that Hans knew nothing about spelling, mathematics, music or anything else, but only knew how to follow the cues given unconsciously by his master.

Another horse-owner in Germany, a man named Herr Krall, still was convinced that horses were capable of mastering complex problems and set out to prove his point with an Arabian stallion named Muhamed.

Muhamed's learning proceeded with startling rapidity. Within a week he could recognize numbers such as 4 or 6 and go to the wall blackboard and point to them with his nose. Within two weeks he could reply that 3 plus 5 equals 8. The following week he was successfully multiplying 6 times 3 and getting 18.

By the end of six weeks Muhamed could figure problems perplexing to the human, such as: $\frac{(3\times4)+\sqrt{36}}{3}=6.$

Though Muhamed proceeded easily up into the realm of higher mathematics, he didn't catch the knack of talking very well and sometimes came up with gibberish words. And it was also observed that Muhamed could perform his mathematical problems consistently only when someone standing before him knew the correct answer.

Apparently Muhamed always began tapping as soon as he was led before the blackboard. In a few instances it was noticed by sharp-eyed observers that Muhamed would begin tapping out the answer *without even glancing* at the blackboard to see what problem he was supposed to be solving! Another curious fact was that Muhamed could tap out the cube root of 216 just as fast as he could add 1 plus 1.

America too has had its talking horses. One was a Shetland pony called Black Bear that resided in Westchester County, New York. Black Bear could reputedly tell time, make change, add and subtract, and kiss ladies graciously. He was described in admiring terms by scientists.

The most celebrated talking horse in America, however, was a horse named Lady that came to fame in Richmond, Virginia. She became famed for her ability to solve mathematical problems, converse in Chinese, read minds and crack jokes. A psychologist reported to the *Journal of Abnormal and Social Psychology* that

Lady was responsive to mental telepathy. But he added that she evidently did not possess independent reasoning powers, because she couldn't seem to give any answers to questions correctly unless some human being standing near by also knew the answer.

Lady, it was observed, usually kept her eye fixed on her master. One of her most astonishing abilities was to crack jokes and engage in repartee. By an odd coincidence her trainer was also quite a genial joke-cracker. In fact their brands of humor seemed similar. One scientist noted drily that "the responses of the animal invariably impressed me as precisely those which the trainer would have given."

When the famed psychologist E. L. Thorndike reviewed all the facts about talking horses, he concluded:

"All of the counting tricks of those horses depend on the fact that the horse raises a hoof when a certain stimulus is given."

One horse starring in Western movies has been seen heading off a runaway horse all by itself . . . getting down when its master is hurt . . . pushing badmen onto the master's fist . . . and closing doors with its nose.

The significant fact to consider, however, is that such horses have full-time trainers teaching them "tricks." Most of the feats could be accounted for by simple learning. And under the scientific "law of parsimony" propounded by Lloyd Morgan, "In no case may we interpret an action as the outcome of the exercise of a higher mental faculty, if it can be interpreted as the outcome of one which stands lower in the psychological scale."

How does the horse perform on some of the standard IQ tests where the problems cannot be solved except by the use of intelligence of a high order? Professor Frank Beach has this to say:

"The horse makes a miserable showing in intelligence tests that any self-respecting pig can pass with ease."

In one test, many animals including the horse were subjected to the tough Multiple Choice Test. In this an animal faces four doors in an arc. One of those doors is unlocked so that the animal can go through it and get food. The problem is to figure which is the unlocked door. It varies. However, there is one helpful clue. The door that was unlocked in the last trial is *never* unlocked in the succeeding trial. Knowledge of that, at least, reduces the choice to three doors.

To learn to avoid that one door requires some pretty heavy thinking, for an animal. It requires the use of "inference" and the grasping of an abstract idea.

In 100 trials the human subjects and the monkeys were able to catch the idea of avoiding this door. Of the dogs and cats tried on this problem, only 14% of the dogs and 9% of the cats succeeded in learning to avoid the door in 100 trials, but at least most of them learned to go systematically from one door to the next until they found one open.

HAVE A SEAT

Notice how the trainer coaxes the horse to remain is a seated position. A horse is capable of learning to obey commands, but he cannot think for himself.

The horse, however, would keep going back to a door over and over before it had tried all of them, and showed little glimmering of systematic thought. Maier and Schneirla in their textbook, *Principles of Animal Psychology,* state: "Only the horse demonstrated what may be called stereotyped behavior, in that it repeatedly tried the same door." The horse and the gopher ended up in a near-tie for last place on this test of higher learning!

In another experiment, reported in the *Journal of Comparative Psychology,* horses were matched against cows in a fairly simple association test. There were three food boxes. One contained food. The problem was whether the horse could learn to associate food with a bucket placed by the box containing food. At first a two-quart bucket was used. Here very few of the horses caught the idea at all. Then a larger 17-quart bucket was used.

After hundreds of trials the horses were able to go to the box that had a pail by it, with an average error of .23. On the same test, cows learned to regard the bucket as a cue with only a .15 error.

In nature the wild horse was a *hunted* animal rather than a *hunting* animal, such as the dog and cat were. This distinction helps account not only for the horse's nature but for the peculiar arrangement of its eyes. The dog and cat have binocular vision such as we have. Their eyes are set in front of the head and can be readily brought to bear jointly on a single object, thus giving precision of vision. In contrast, the horse's eyes (like those of another hunted animal, the deer) are on the sides of its head. This gives a wider field of vision for detecting enemies, but there is less precision. Usually it sees an object with only one eye.

The whole psychology of the wild horse was geared to flight. It didn't even have the horns of a deer or steer to defend itself. This impulse to flee combined with the wide but imprecise vision gave the horse a high-strung, skittish personality.

The horse is a noble creature to look at. And we all feel magnificently enhanced when we can sit with a fine steed between our legs. But we should not let these facts obscure from us the horse's essential nature. The horse not only has a modest mentality but has a strong tendency to go berserk when startled. One shrewd student of the horse concluded:

"The trouble is that a good horse is a bundle of emotions, tied up with a short-circuited nervous system. A spirited horse will shy so violently at a fluttering bit of paper that it will fall down and break a leg." In the early days of the auto literally thousands of horses in harness went leaping up a bank—buggy and all—when an auto approached.

A horse's wide and unreliable vision combined with its high-strung temperament compels it to wear those ridiculous blinders. Otherwise its mind would wander hopelessly from its work.

At the winter quarters of the Ringling Circus visitors can watch many of the animals being trained in stunts for the coming season. Visitors are barred, however, from watching horses being trained. Why? Because horses are so nervous and so easily distracted that they can't concentrate if visitors are present.

In the case of fire in a stable a horse, as is well known, must be blindfolded before it can be led out. A cow, in contrast, will walk out sensibly like an orderly school child answering fire drill, and a mule will break its halter and kick down a door to escape a fire. During a fire in Kentucky about 30 fine thoroughbreds were led from a

"THE BRAINS OF A DONKEY"

The next time you use this expression, be sure you know what you mean. The donkey is no fool at all. In fact, he's a genius compared with the most brilliant horse that ever lived.

burning stable into a yard. But when in the excitement they were left in the yard untied, many of them went charging back into the fire, like moths racing toward a flame.

The mule shows more sense than a horse in another way—in eating. The mule will eat only what it needs. But many horses overeat, or overdrink after a hard day. They often make such hogs of themselves that their bellies become bloated.

All this of course does not make the horse any less lovable or admirable. We all feel a tingling of excitement when we see a herd of horses galloping, and we feel a tug at the heart when a horse nuzzles our hand for sugar. But we shouldn't let our emotions confuse us into imputing to the noble-looking animal intelligence it doesn't really have.

9. The Wisdom of Cats

DR. Gustav Eckstein, the noted physiologist of the University of Cincinnati, has a passion for observing animals in their natural environment. One day he heard of a remarkable cat named Willy. Every Monday evening at exactly 7:45 Willy was said to go through an astonishing ritual. Dr. Eckstein could not believe the tale—until he spent several Mondays following Willy and charting his movements. Here is what Dr. Eckstein observed:

Willy appeared to be a very ordinary, matter-of-fact cat most of the week. Every night he would lie dozing on the porch after supper. But on Monday nights, at precisely 7:45, Willy would get up from his favorite dozing spot and walk very purposefully out to the pavement. When he came to intersections he would wait, if the light was red, for the green light.

Several blocks away he would walk up a grassy slope to a hospital. He would then continue directly to a spot underneath a window of the nurses' dining room. There he would leap up to the window's ledge, and spend the

I DIDN'T DO IT!

This sweet look of innocence would have done Tom Sawyer justice. The crime: tearing a pillow to see what's inside. "Why didn't somebody *tell* me it was feathers?"

next two hours watching with fascination the activities going on inside, where a group of ladies were playing bingo.

These ladies always played bingo in this room on Monday night, and only Monday night. Willy could not have taken this trip each Monday night because of any reward of food, for there was no reward. Also he didn't take the trip for the companionship of other cats, because he invariably was the only cat present. Apparently he just liked to watch ladies jump up and holler, as they do at bingo games. When the game was over, Willy always went directly home.

How did Willy know when Monday 7:45 arrived each week? Dr. Eckstein doesn't know. Willy may have been aided by some association cues, but it seems that he did have a natural time sense, because he always appeared at the door for breakfast at about 8:10 each

morning. He apparently knew his master would leave
for the day a few minutes later.

Willy, you will note, found amusement in watching
the antics of Man. However, Willy was not particularly
friendly with people at the house where he lived. He
would tolerate being petted but wouldn't go out of his
way to get it.

In this he was being a typical cat. In contrast, another cat whose feats have been reported, was far from
typical. This cat, Wendell, seemed really to adore his
mistress, and to be eager to win her approval.

Each night Wendell worked energetically capturing
mice and moles. When his mistress opened her back
door each morning she saw, lined up beside the proud

Wendell, all the mice and moles he had caught the night before. As far as could be found, Wendell never ate the mice and moles. He had never developed a taste for them. He captured them at night just to show off.

In this respect Wendell was an extraordinarily untypical cat. The fact that he was raised as an "only cat" in a household that also had a dog may have influenced him to be more eager to seek Man's favor than is considered to be in good taste by most cats.

It is not quite accurate to call a cat domesticated, in the sense that the dog and horse are domesticated, because she is neither exploited nor abject in her loyalty. Cats are rarely "loyal" in the sense that a dog is loyal.

The cat lets Man support her. But unlike the dog, she is no hand-licker. She is like a human lady golddigger in that she lets Man court her with catnip leaves. She may reward her human admirer with a purr but will continue leading her own life. She wouldn't think of showing gratitude by performing tricks or leaping all over her benefactor.

Futhermore, unlike Man's other great good friend, the horse, the cat is no sweating serf of Man. The only labor she condescends to perform is to catch mice and rats, and that's fun.

Despite her aloofness, the cat still has millions of human admirers, mainly because she makes good company. An organization called Cat Fancy—devoted to adoring cats—has 51 clubs scattered around the country, with national officers.

Whenever cat-lovers get together the discussion usually gets around, sooner or later, to the question: "Which

NO SEARCHING INTELLECT HERE
An intelligent expression on her face doesn't make this cat a braintruster. As a matter of fact, the dispute as to which is smarter—dog or cat—still rages, and the dog is certainly no quiz kid.

is smarter, the cat or the dog?" They naturally argue in favor of the cat.

Some claim there is no argument. As evidence of this they point to the fact that Dr. Albert Payson Terhune, the great dog-lover, is alleged to have conceded that cats are smarter than dogs. The evidence that is said to have cinched that matter with him was the behavior of a cat and dog at a water faucet. When the dog was thirsty it would wait by the faucet until someone turned it on. The cat, in contrast, would turn the tap by pushing the lever with her paws.

This of course is not conclusive evidence, as the cat may have learned to turn on the faucet by accident while climbing on it.

Psychologists seem to feel the cat and dog are pretty closely matched in intelligence. Dr. Riess states that the cat appears to be smarter than the dog on tests where vision is a major element. On the puzzle box and the multiple choice test of finding the open door, results show that the dog has a slight edge. But psychologists suspect this may be due, at least in part, to the dog's fantastic eagerness to please the human testers. Dr. Edward L. Thorndike made this comment about dogs on tests:

"More than any other domestic animal, they direct their attention to us, and what we do."

Many years ago Dr. Thorndike, then a young man just out of Harvard, became fed up with unsubstantiated eulogies about the cat's intelligence and set out to get reliable information by watching cats in action. He was a pioneer in using the problem box. The cat could open the box by pulling a looped string.

In many tests he put a hungry cat inside the wire cage and placed chunks of fish outside. At the sight of the fish the cat typically engaged in a mad scramble to get out of the box. It bit and clawed at all parts of the cage. (In the energy of its efforts to escape the cage it surpassed the dog.)

For no reason in particular, as far as Thorndike could see, the cat would finally catch its claws in the looped string and the door would swing open. Gradually in repeated trials, the cat would eliminate useless movements. Ultimately it would paw the loops as soon as the test began. Thus every cat mastered the box. Thorndike was convinced, however, that the cat did it through trial and error and had no more idea how it had opened the box than we understand what happens when we "turn on" an incandescent bulb by pushing a button.

Later experimenters have felt Thorndike was too severe in his judgment. They believe the cat's solution of the puzzle box was not so random and haphazard as Thorndike seemed to think.

Like the dog, the cat appears to be unable to learn by imitating another cat. In one test an experimenter put two cats into a problem box at once. One of the cats had already mastered the box and knew how to open it in a jiffy. The other cat was new to the box.

What happened? The experienced cat demonstrated how to open the door time after time by pulling the string, but the untrained cat never caught a glimmering of the idea, even though it was frantic to get the pieces of fish lying outside. It was only when the untrained cat was left in the box itself and had a chance to claw all around the cage that, by trial and error, it eventually learned to pull the string.

This evidence runs counter to the widespread belief that mother cats "teach" their young how to catch prey. A mother lion is said to train her young by bringing home wounded antelope and showing the young how to pounce on the antelope and kill it. Likewise, there is a widely held notion that mother cats bring home crippled mice and "teach" their kittens how to catch the mouse. In the same way both lion and cat mothers are said to take their young on hunting expeditions to teach them how it is done.

What actually happens, apparently, is somewhat different. The mother helps the young to learn—but they do not learn by imitating their mother. They learn mainly by *participation*. The mother's contribution is to put them in situations where they are likely to get good experience.

It has also been widely thought that cats have a natural instinct to catch and kill mice. That, it develops, is not the case. A kitten that had never seen a mouse before was put into a cage with a mouse. They soon became great friends, played rough-and-tumble games together without either getting scratched. An old, experienced cat was then placed into the cage with them and immediately killed the mouse. Then the kitten was

again put with a mouse. Still it treated the mouse as a companion rather than an object of prey. It was only after several repetitions that the kitten began pouncing on the mouse and treated it more roughly until it killed it. (In this re-education of the kitten, imitation did apparently play some role, though it may merely have originated the idea of playing roughly.)

The above experiment indicates that there is some factual validity for the children's story, *Peter Churchmouse*, about the mouse and the kitten who, unaware that they were supposed to be deadly enemies, got along together in beautiful harmony.

One investigator tested very exhaustively the cat-rat relationship, and became convinced that the two are not hereditary enemies at all. Rat-killing appears to be an acquired trait. He concluded that it is just as natural for cats and rats to love each other as to hate each other.

Twenty kittens were raised in isolation. When they were placed in areas where there were rats, only a few became rat-killers. Of 18 kittens that were reared in isolation and given rats as playmates, only three ever became rat-killers and even those three did not kill their cage mates. In contrast, of the 21 kittens raised in an environment where rat-killing was common, practically all of them became rat-killers at an early age.

Some of these kittens were raised on a vegetarian diet. This did not affect their tendency to kill rats when raised in a rat-killing environment. But they did not eat the rats they killed.

Why, you may ask, do cats become rat-killers if they don't have an instinct for it? The explanation apparently is that Nature has predisposed cats to be small-animal

NOT SO VICIOUS

These kittens aren't spying on rats at all. Before they start attacking rats, they will have to be taught that they are "enemies."

killers by endowing the cat with certain features. New-born kittens have claws, and they have a tendency to play and to leap at any small moving object. Maier and Schneirla say that the rat-killing response of cats "seems to depend upon a tendency to be excited by, and thus to pounce upon, a small moving object, the eating of which is due to accidentally tasting blood when claws and teeth are sunk into some such object."

The fact that a cat has to learn how to catch animals, and is not born with a ready-made instinct for it, shows that the cat is moderately well up the scale of animal intelligence. It has a fairly adaptable, alert mind. If, for example, a mother cat has five kittens and one is removed when the mother's back is turned, the mother will miss that kitten and search for it. That is an indication of a counting ability.

On the other hand an indication of the cat's mental limitations is found in its brain weight. It should be emphasized here that the brain weight is no accurate index of intelligence. A human moron, for example, can have as heavy a brain as a human genius. However, the ratio of brain weight to body weight does hold some significance to scientists. Some of the lower animals really have pea-sized brains.

A man's body as a whole typically weighs 35 times more than his brain. The body of a chimpanzee (one of the very brightest of all animals) weighs 75 times more than its brain. And the body of a cat weighs 110 times more than its brain, which may indicate roughly how far down the scale cats are from apes.

10. Wild vs. Tame Animals

E have just seen the fair-to-dismal showing that Man's three best friends, the dog, horse and cat, make on objective intelligence tests. All three are domesticated. This raises the question whether domestication has any effect on an animal's intelligence. Many psychologists believe it does have an effect—and a damaging one. Domesticity dulls their wits.

Dr. Bernard Riess expressed serious doubt that Man did the horse, the dog and the cat a favor when he adopted them and started taking care of their needs. Wild animals almost uniformly do better on laboratory problems than tame animals. When I asked Dr. Riess why, he said:

"Probably because the tame animals have never had to hustle for a living."

He cited an experience he had had in testing the intelligence of cats on the puzzle box. In the test he used several alley cats he had captured himself or gotten from animal pounds. These cats were technically tame, but they had been on their own in the alleys of New York so long that they were scrawny and savage.

Somehow word leaked out that he was using alley cats for his experiments in probing animal intelligence. A well-to-do lady who heard this came bustling to his laboratory with her purebred pedigreed Siamese. She explained that she feared the uncouth alley creatures were not fair representatives of the cat's true intelligence.

Actually the alley cats had been doing quite well. However, Dr. Riess agreed to let the Siamese have a chance at the puzzle box, to demonstrate his fair-mindedness. When the lady's beautiful cream-raised Siamese was placed in front of the puzzle box with the chunks of fish inside, it revealed complete indifference. It would walk away. Then they arranged the test so that the cat could not walk away. When this was done, the cat sat down and stared with mild interest at the fish. It clawed around the box idly for a few minutes, then settled down for a snooze.

Dr. Riess suggested helpfully that he hold the cat a few days and keep it on a rigid diet so that it would get good and hungry. Then he would try again. This horrified the lady and she took her darling home. It was just as well, for Dr. Riess suspects the Siamese had become so mentally sluggish from easy living that even hunger would not stimulate its mental machinery much at this late date.

The domestic cat has the same basic character traits as its wild ancestors. The lion, the wildcat, the puma and the pussy cat all reveal to some extent the same independence and love of comfort characteristic of the cat. It is probably this trait that first led to its downfall. It found domesticity comfortable, but now has paid for this comfort with mental sluggishness.

The horse likewise has been corrupted by domesticity. Ever since the invention of the bridle tens of centuries ago, the horse has not had to do any independent figuring. Its movements have been completely managed by Man.

In contrast the jackass has never been tamed and pampered by Man to the extent that the horse has been. The jackass is generally credited with having a more

NO "DUMB BUNNY" HE

This bunny, whose ability to survive hasn't been stunted by domestication, remembered correctly that the carrot was always in the light-shaded box. Here he is considering his choice before making a move.

nimble, astute mind. One man who had made a study of
the horse family reached this extreme conclusion:

"A jackass is a genius compared to the most brilliant
horse that ever lived. So is a mule, despite the strain of
idiocy in his family." (The mule is a cross between a
jackass and a horse.)

Farmers who have used both the horse and the mule
in farm work usually will prefer the horse, but that is
not because of the horse's superior intelligence. Rather
it is because the mule is more independent and less
tractable than the horse, and thus is apt to cause annoy-
ing delays.

Animals in the wild have to keep themselves at razor-
sharp alertness in order to survive. Life under domes-

tication dulls that edge. Perhaps there is no better illustration of this than the fate of the dog. It is no accident that among the smartest dogs are the shepherds and collies. They are the hard-working dogs that still have to live by their wits.

In the wild, the timber wolves and coyotes (or prairie wolves) are deeply respected for their cunning. Dogs of course are descended from the wolf. Many acts of ingenuity have been authenticated. Wolves have been seen employing several varieties of the ambush. In the North Woods, the arctic wolves hunting in packs have chased so many caribou over cliffs that it can hardly be accidental. Deliberate strategy apparently is involved.

The little coyote, intensely despised by our sheepmen and cattle ranchers, has been described in at least one scientific journal as "the smartest animal alive."

Man, in his fury, often calls the coyote a coward, but that is a subjective, prejudiced opinion from our particular viewpoint. Certainly the coyote is crafty and a genius at adapting himself to all conditions. He has even been known to hitch rides on wagons or moving flatcars.

Scientists who analyzed the contents of 15,000 coyote stomachs found that the main diet is jack rabbit—and it takes a clever animal to catch many jack rabbits. But also in the coyote stomachs they found bits of automobile tires, harness buckles, horned toads, wildcats, armadillos, skunks, grasshoppers, turtles, rattlesnakes, bumblebees and porcupines. In short, the goat is a fussy eater compared to the coyote.

NO MANNERS HERE

This cub isn't too meticulous about how he eats. Although born in a zoo, he retains most of the instincts of the wild and is alert to every threat to his survival.

For decades the Federal government has conducted a grim war to exterminate the coyote. Millions have been killed. The government trappers use the cyanide-gun and other deadly devices with their traps, yet today the coyote is flourishing from Alaska to Central America, and is almost impossible to tame.

Men who sat out trap lines for coyote often find that every trap on the line has been sprung. And when they investigate they frequently find coyotes sneaking along behind them. As with the raccoon, the coyote can best be trapped by playing on his great curiosity. (Curiosity is an index of intelligence.) One trapper reports he has had excellent luck catching coyotes by burying an old alarm clock near a trap. The coyote becomes so intrigued trying to find what causes the ticking that it steps accidentally onto the hidden trap.

One evidence of the coyote's wizardry is the great number of tales involving the coyote in Mexican and Indian folklore. In popular Mexican speech the phrase *"muy coyote"* means plenty shrewd, especially in a crafty way. America's outstanding authority on the coyote is believed to be Professor J. Frank Dobie of Texas. After spending many years studying the coyote, he reported some of his findings in his book, *The Voice of the Coyote*. Coyotes, he says, know how to disguise themselves . . . how to play jokes and to trick other animals . . . how to imitate the sounds they hear . . . how to get through barbed wire fences . . . how to hunt in groups.

In fact, the coyotes have highly organized strategies for hunting. When they are stalking antelope they run in relays to wear down the antelope. On the trail of jack rabbit they surround a flock of jack rabbit and drive them into an ever-narrowing circle just as men do.

Another naturalist, A. G. A. Russell, reported to the American Museum of Natural History an example of coyote ingenuity which he studied through his binoculars on a wintery day in Canada. He was observing an old elk bull trying to graze on a mountain slope. The ground was covered by a hard crust of snow. The hungry elk would paw loose the crust with his hard hoof in order to graze on the grass under the snow.

As the naturalist watched, he saw a coyote warily approaching the elk. The elk saw him but went on grazing. The coyote came closer and soon was within a few feet of the elk. As the elk would paw up a fresh crust of snow the coyote would lunge forward and pounce upon *mice* uncovered by the elk. For a half-hour the coyote let the grazing elk serve as a mouse-digger for him. Russell relates:

"Several times I saw him duck right under the elk's belly and snatch a mouse from under his feet."

The coyote eats mice, but he also eats calves. Cattlemen in the Southwest complain that coyotes are killing their calves at a rate that has become serious. In earlier years the coyotes didn't attack calves. Why the change? The explanation reveals something about the incredible adaptability of coyotes, and also of the effect of excessive domestication on animals.

In early days the coyotes didn't bother calves because the thin, stringy, wild, range cows could defend their calves very effectively. In contrast, the highly-bred, plump modern cow, which man has created to provide juicier sirloins, is too clumsy and inept to ward off an attack by coyotes. And the coyotes have learned of this man-made weakness.

Archibald Rutledge, the well-known naturalist, contends that "when wild creatures are given artificial security they never fail to deteriorate—certainly in a physical way and, in a sense, in a moral way as well. They become soft, careless, dull-witted, degenerate, losing that superb edge which, in the wilds, with life a constant battle and danger ever near, they must possess if they are to survive."

11. The Brain Trust of the Animal Kingdom

O_N almost every animal IQ test that has been devised—whether it is a test of simple dexterity or of sheer braininess—the winners by a long shot are members of the monkey family.

When we come to the monkeys, psychologists feel fairly safe in using the terms "reasoning" and "thinking," without hedging or wondering, to describe behavior they see. Professor Beach says of the monkeys and apes: "Some of their reactions are so reminiscent of human reasoning that the same term seems applicable to both."

In our popular language the word monkey is synonymous with "fool." A dictionary before me states that the word *monkey* is often used as "a name of contempt." Ever since Man has learned that the monkey is a fairly close relative he has felt rather nervous about being seen with monkeys or even looking at them too closely. Let us here face up to the facts about monkey wisdom.

Technically, a monkey is a quadrumanous (or four-handed) mammal. There are 57 varieties of monkey, or primate, and then some. They range from the tail-swinging South American monkeys, such as the cebus monkey, to Old World monkeys, such as the baboon.

The elite of the monkeys however are the large tailless monkeys known as anthropoid or Great Apes. These apes are semi-erect, with long arms, man-like hands, and man-like faces. The three Great Apes include the sweet, lovable orangutan . . . the wise-guyish, extroverted chimpanzee . . . and the quiet, tidy, introverted gorilla.

The orang is known to the inhabitants of its native Borneo as "Man of the Woods." It has enormously long arms and is distinguished from the other apes by its very long reddish-brown hair. The young orangs look very "human" and appealing, but adult orangs get deep folds around their faces that make them look less human. The other two Great Apes, the chimp and the gorilla, are found in Equatorial Africa, and both have black hair.

Both the orang and the chimp weigh somewhat less than a man and are shorter, whereas the gorilla is a foot or so taller than a man, weighs about 400 pounds, and has the strength of a dozen husky men. The gorilla's sunken eyes and its massive, pointed head give it a fierce, brutal look that doesn't fairly represent its basically gentle nature.

A fourth monkey that is sometimes classified as an ape is the small tailless gibbon, whose exceptionally long arms swing it gracefully and swiftly through the treetops. However, it looks so much like an ordinary monkey that most zoologists don't accept it as a true Great Ape.

Although Man most closely resembles the Great Apes, he is not descended from them. Most zoologists now believe that Man's nearest direct relative is one of the very lowest forms of pre-monkey primates, probably the saucer-eyed little tarsier. The Great Apes evolved on another branch of the family tree and so are more properly our *cousins* rather than our *ancestors*.

Let us look at a few of the ways in which members of the great monkey family demonstrate their intellectual superiority over all other animals.

Monkeys will solve in a few seconds a puzzle box that will baffle dogs for hours. The standard puzzle boxes,

A LONG, SAD LOOK AT THE WORLD

If you were to present these six chimps with a problem, they'd solve it in a jiffy. But let them sit idle for too long and their natural curiosity will get them into mischief.

where the animal must turn buttons, slide bolts or push down levers, are so easy for a monkey that he quickly becomes bored by them. It is only when you introduce tricky locks such as vertical hooks, T-latches and combination serial locks that the monkey has to scratch his head. Once he learns the secret of a lock, he soon opens it without fuss in later trials.

I have mentioned that the monkeys and apes can "think." It requires a form of thinking, for example, to co-operate with another animal in solving a problem, especially when the co-operation is deliberate and premeditated. Here's an example. A box of food was placed outside the cage of a chimpanzee. It was too far away to reach, but a rope was attached. The chimp pulled at the rope, but the box was so heavy that he could barely budge it. So what happened? The chimp in the test signaled a second chimp in the cage and persuaded him to come over and give him a hand on the rope. The two of them together, tugging in unison, were able to pull the food within reach. That required real animal brainwork.

Another mark of monkey superiority is that monkeys are said to be the only mammals that have true social instincts. It was Seneca who originally observed that "Man is a social animal." Monkeys are the first mammals to be highly sociable in the sense that Man is sociable. Young monkeys, for example, stick together and maintain a strong family spirit long after they are capable of pushing out for themselves. Sympathy, as Romanes observed, is "more strongly marked in monkeys than in any other animal, not even excepting the dog." A sick monkey is waited upon with great anxiety and tenderness by its friends, who will even sacrifice their favorite dainties in order to offer them to their sick comrade.

The monkeys also reveal their mental superiority by the swiftness with which they learn lessons. Let's compare their behavior concerning traps with that of mice. In my home we were greatly bothered by mice who came up into the kitchen through holes near the kitchen sink.

Several years ago I bought an ordinary little mouse trap which I set with cheese bait near the hole. In that one bloodstained little trap I have caught at least 85 mice. During a recent fall season I found a mouse in that trap every morning for nine consecutive days.

In Durban, South Africa, a man was greatly bothered by monkeys that invaded his house and garden at night, so he began setting monkey traps, baited with bananas. The first day he caught 20 monkeys. The second day, he caught one monkey. After that he never caught another.

Monkeys are also highly adaptable, especially to Man's ways. Any monkey can learn bathroom behavior, and all monkeys are fascinated for hours by the sound of a flushing toilet.

Monkeys can count, though in this they are apparently not markedly superior to certain other animals. If you hand a monkey marbles he can be easily trained to give you any number you request up to five.

We have said that one index of intelligence is curiosity. Monkeys, like coons and coyotes, have this to a marked degree. Officials of Chicago's Brookfield Zoo faced a great problem in rounding up the baboons on their special island to bring them indoors for the winter.

The baboons—only moderately bright as monkeys go—
went scurrying up trees. Finally the officials figured a
way to lure them within reach by playing on their natural curiosity. They placed an ordinary doghouse on the
island and inside it they put a big mirror. Also as a final
attraction they painted a picture of a banana on the
mirror.

Soon the baboons were swarming around the doghouse to get a look at themselves in the mirror. By the
time all the baboons were rounded up it was found that
there were teeth marks on the mirror. Some of the
baboons had evidently been trying to eat the painted
banana.

One great advantage monkeys have over all other
animals is, of course, their man-like hands. One of the
tricks they have learned is to use their hands and arms
to throw objects. In one house that wild monkeys invaded, they got a stack of phonograph records and had
a delirious time scaling them out of the upstairs window.

Baboons that were tested by a psychologist developed
great accuracy in hurling grapes, overhand, at the psychologist, without hitting the bars. In the jungle baboons use stones as missiles in fighting. And certain
monkeys use stones to crack nuts.

It is in the use of tools (or instrumentation) that
members of the monkey family most clearly show their
superiority over all other animals. Furthermore, it is in
the use of tools that apes clearly show their superiority
of intelligence over the lower monkeys.

Ordinary monkeys are markedly inferior to apes in
solving problems by using sticks, boxes, etc. The average
monkey, for example, will move a box under a sus-

TIME OUT FOR A SMOKE

This old orangutan at the St. Louis Zoo must have his 12-cent cigar
every afternoon, or he starts to wreck the place.

pended banana in order to reach it, only under the most favorable circumstances, and will never think of stacking boxes to reach the food. Usually monkeys will get the idea of using poles to pull in food only when the pole is laid close by in a suggestive position.

The Great Apes, in contrast, not only use tools freely, but even make their own tools. They will break a branch of a tree and use it as a tool to rake in food. In one test several bamboo sticks were laid inside a chimpanzee's cage. But all the sticks proved to be too short to reach the food outside the cage. So what did the chimp do? After a few minutes of experimenting he managed to stick the end of one bamboo stick inside the other so that the two made one long pole. With this contrivance he reached out and raked in the grapes.

Even among the Great Apes there are great differences of talent in the use of tools. Orangutans catch the idea of stacking boxes to reach a banana only with difficulty. Usually they have to be shown how to do it. Chimpanzees, in contrast, will get the idea of stacking boxes to build a high platform without any demonstration, and in fact will stack as many as four boxes on top of each other, if necessary, in order to build a platform high enough to permit them to reach the suspended banana.

The close physiological similarity of apes to Man is indicated by the fact that the ape is the only creature in the entire animal kingdom capable of catching the common cold. A chimp with a head cold looks just as miserable as a wheezy human.

In the past when I have written about the superior intelligence of monkeys, many dog-lovers and horse-

A CLEAN HIT

Would you do as well if you had never had a hammer in your hand? Cookie had seen his keeper drive a nail before. When Cookie was handed the hammer, he quickly put it to correct use.

lovers have sent me sarcastic letters. If the monkeys are so bright, they ask, why hasn't Man put them to work at useful tasks, such as the horse and dog perform?

I can't vouch for what goes on inside a monkey's mind, but I suspect that one reason he doesn't slave for man is that he is too smart to be anybody's stooge. At any rate, ordinary work profoundly bores a monkey. Man has almost always had very unsatisfactory results in trying to domesticate monkeys. Perhaps the monkey has deliberately gold-bricked. Consider the curious status of the baboon.

Today the baboon has a nasty, disagreeable disposi-

tion in the presence of Man and becomes obstinate when Man tries to teach him even the simplest tricks. The American Museum of Natural History's publication, *Animal Kingdom,* recently called the baboon "a rather savage, intractable animal."

Yet 4,000 years ago the baboon was apparently a docile, domesticated animal! Egyptian wall paintings on tombs in the vicinity of Beni Hasan in the Nile valley show baboon-like monkeys gathering figs and palm leaves for their human masters.

Today only a few monkeys have permitted themselves to be pressed into the service of Man. The pig-tailed macaque is used in Malaya and Sumatra to pick coconuts. The owner ties a cord around the macaque's waist and takes it to a coconut palm tree. The monkey swiftly shinnies up the tree and goes from one nut to another. It places its hands on a nut, then looks at the master for advice as to whether the nut is sufficiently ripe. If the owner tugs the rope, the monkeys goes on to another nut, but if the owner shouts "all right," the macaque twists the nut around until the stalk is broken, and then lets it fall.

In Ethiopia certain monkeys are taught to serve as torchbearers at human supper parties. They stand in a row on a raised bench and hold lights until the departure of the guests, when they are rewarded by receiving their own supper. Even as torchbearers, however, monkeys don't appear to be too satisfactory. Playful monkeys frequently disrupt the human supper parties by tossing their lighted torches in the midst of the guests.

As far as can be found, none of the Great Apes has ever been successfully domesticated. At least the apes have consistently refused to be drafted for constructive labor. Chimps don't mind riding bicycles in circuses because they enjoy showing off and find bike-riding a lot of fun. However, even at this they occasionally remind their human trainers that they are nobody's stooge.

In one act a lady chimp was trained to ride a two-seated bike around the ring, stop and pick up a male chimp as a passenger and continue around the ring. One day she added an interesting variation all her own. When she reached the male, she dismounted, went over to the male, proceeded to beat the daylights out of him, then got back on her bike and resumed her act. Perhaps she had some grievance against the male. Or perhaps she simply wanted to enliven the act by adding a dash of her own improvisation. At any rate, she effectively reminded her audience that she was no silly old trained seal.

12.   Champion Quiz Kid of Them All

SCIENTISTS have speculated for years about which is the brainiest creature in the whole animal kingdom. The evidence now indicates that, at least on the basis of the IQ tests available, the chimpanzee heads the class.

Chimpanzees can perform feats of reasoning that are beyond the depth of many primitive human beings on the globe. And in tests they frequently out-reason typical five-year-old American youngsters.

The average chimp can saw wood, hammer nails and use the screwdriver about as well as my young son and can easily be taught to eat with a fork. He enjoys a good cigar as well as the next man and takes quite naturally to eating at a table with grown-up human beings.

In case you're thinking of having a chimp out to dinner, you'll find him a very entertaining, appreciative guest, but I warn you that he has one habit that may present a social problem to a fastidious hostess: when chimps start to enjoy themselves at a dinner table, they are apt to forget their good manners and casually put their feet on the table while they eat.

COCKTAIL TIME

Like his human counterpart, this baby is delighted at the idea of drinking his milk from a bottle.

Almost all chimps are friendly and have a great zest for life. They have the best disposition of all the apes, and enjoy Man's company.

Chimpanzees are so bright—and so human—that they seem to resent being cooped up in cages *just like animals.* They consider their cages an insult, and although they show little interest in running away from human society when they have the opportunity, they do devote a great deal of thought to breaking out of their unspeakable cages. Some have become talented jailbreakers.

Wendy, for example, always showed great cunning and persistence at "busting out" of her stoutly built, heavily-wired cage. She apparently plotted her jailbreaks with the care of a Sing Sing inmate tunneling his way under prison walls. To produce a hole big enough for her lady-sized body she had to unbend hundreds of heavy wires. This unbending was not only a tough mental problem in itself for an animal, but it required ex-

traordinary persistence and purposefulness because it took many hours of patient work.

Furthermore, this unbending operation had to be carried on without attracting the attention of the human guardians. Wendy always picked a spot in a remote, dimly-lighted corner of her cage. She not only pursued her illegal plans surreptitiously while no human was watching, but she carried out elaborate diversionary strategies while they were near. She would make extraordinarily loud noises, exude friendliness toward her human guardians, and pretend to be deeply preoccupied with legal activities.

The problem of making an escape hole often required days of work. As Wendy untwisted the wire ends she would—again showing cunning—leave the wire in place so that her human guardians would not notice her plot. Only when she had untwisted enough wires to provide

an exit would she push the wire mesh back and make a bolt for freedom. These escapes almost invariably occurred at night when no one was watching. Once free, she would loiter happily in the woods near by until her human keepers picked her up and took her back to her three square meals of free food a day.

In a few cases where chimps have stacked all the boxes available and still couldn't reach the banana, they have then picked up a long stick, mounted the boxes and then knocked down the banana with the stick. It should be remembered that many three-year-old human children still can't get the idea of stacking even a few blocks to build a tower.

In using sticks to pull in food outside their cage, chimps have reached out to get a short stick, then used the short stick to pull in a longer stick. With the long stick they succeeded in raking in the food.

Chimps can not only count quite a few numbers, but seem to have some idea of multiplication. One female would not only hand you the number of straws you asked for, up to five, but sometimes would bend a straw in half and then try to pass it off as two straws.

Memory is one sign of intelligence, and chimps appear to have extraordinary memories. In one instance a man spanked a young chimp who had been caught stealing. The chimp did not see that man until two years later, but when she did, she leaped on the astonished man (who himself had forgotten the incident) and proceeded to give him a bad pummeling.

Chimpanzees have been tested on many standard toys. One is the long block which has square, round and triangular holes. The problem is to put square, round and

ROUND PEGS IN ROUND HOLES

Peg puzzles, such as this one, are employed to teach children to reason for themselves. As you can see, this chimp hasn't much to learn.

triangular pegs in the right holes. Chimps can learn this faster than many youngsters.

One adult chimp at a laboratory learned to master a set of tough discrimination problems where he had to keep five distinct factors—such as size, shape and color—in mind in making a choice between two objects.

Professor Harry F. Harlow, head of the University of Wisconsin's large primate laboratory, has done a good deal of work in comparing the intelligence of apes and children. He recently stated that in some of the simpler problems "the smartest chimps learned faster than the dullest children" and that in some of the more complex situations the animals "actually did better than most of the children."

One bright chimp became a whiz at picking similarities and differences, which is one of the most difficult mental processes for either animals or human beings. Most IQ tests for youngsters include such problems.

In his test, Professor Harlow laid out nine objects of various colors and shapes. The chimp learned to pick out all the red objects, all the blue ones, etc.

Professor Harlow has concluded that thinking ability is to a large extent the result of training, and human beings eventually outdistance apes because they get much more training and experience in meeting problems before they mature.

Chimpanzees are so much like human beings not only in their intellectual make-up but in their emotional behavior and in their physical make-up that scientists have found them valuable in trying to get a better understanding of Man. In a sense they are simplified hu-

BATTLE OF WITS

Two youngsters, aged three, attack the same problem. The contestant on the left showed the greater skill in matching up pegs with holes, but he quickly got bored and had a more difficult time keeping his mind on the problem.

man beings. One of the world's outstanding psychobiological laboratories for the study of apes has been the Yerkes Laboratories of Primate Biology at Orange Park, Florida, where at any one time more than 50 apes have been under study. This laboratory, sponsored by both Yale and Harvard, was founded by one of the great pioneers in comparative psychology, Dr. Robert M. Yerkes.

At Orange Park chimpanzees have been observed and measured from the moment of birth to maturity and they have been tested in a series of situations that were standardized for testing human infants and children by Yale's Dr. Arnold Gesell.

Chimps are born after a gestation of eight months compared to the approximate nine months for human infants. Mother chimps are usually a bit clumsy in handling their first-born and are apt to hold the baby upside down, or dangle it by the umbilical cord, but they become more competent with later babies. Baby chimps who are raised by bottle rather than at the mother's

breast usually become thumb-suckers, just as human babies suck their thumbs.

In the jungle, chimpanzees build a new nest for themselves in some near-by tree every night. When chimpanzees captured from the jungle were transplanted to the Yerkes laboratory, it was found that whenever they had the opportunity they would climb a tree at night and build themselves a nest. However, it was soon observed

LET'S KEEP IT CLEAN

Cookie, a chimp at the St. Louis Zoo, studiously practices the proper use of the broom.

that chimps who were born and raised at the laboratory did not do this. In fact, they showed no inclination toward nest-building.

To comparative psychologists this is very significant. You will recall that the birds we discussed in an earlier chapter would build a perfect nest even though the bird and its ancestors had been reared in isolation from nesting materials. There, we had instinct at work. With the chimps nest-building has to be learned by each individual chimp from its elders. The more an animal has to *learn* in fending for itself, the more it is likely the animal will possess a high order of intelligence. Man, for example, has to learn practically everything he does. Newborn human babies are helpless.

If instinct worked as thoroughly with Man as it does with birds, every human youngster would know by instinct how to build his own bungalow—which is hardly the case.

Most of the psychologists who have studied chimps find that human and chimp infants have a great deal in common for almost a year. Then human youngsters start forging ahead and learning at a much faster rate than chimp youngsters.

Chimps apparently resemble Man even more in their emotional than in their mental or physical make-up. They become deeply annoyed when frustrated. One ape who loved to watch a fat lady cook working became furious when his trainer began shutting a door that closed off the view. At his first opportunity he bit the trainer.

Chimps are highly sociable with both Man and fellow apes. (Some seem to prefer the company of Man to that of other apes.) Also like Man, they love attention.

At zoos the chimps will often make lewd gestures or squirt water to attract the attention of disinterested humans passing by. One of the chimps at the Bronz Zoo acts like a carnival barker in order to draw people (who possibly have popcorn) to his cage. He will bang a bucket on the floor, howl, clap his hands and wave his arms, and leap energetically around the cage, all the time watching the gathering crowd out of the corner of his eye.

When he has collected a sizeable and appreciative crowd he will squat down sociably in front of the cluster of people, stick out his tongue and make an assortment of grotesque faces, meanwhile holding out one hand soliciting tidbits. If he is lucky enough to win a banana he will go off happily to a corner, seat himself comfortably, casually skin the banana and then consume it amid much appreciative lip-smacking.

Like humans, chimps are also great practical jokers. Young chimps, like certain young imps I know, delight in taking flying leaps onto Pa's belly while Pa is asleep. Their pa seems to react the same way I do in believing it is not a bit funny.

At one laboratory the lights suddenly went out one night. They psychologists and attendants were mystified. Who could have turned off the light? The only switch was on a wall several feet from the cage of Jojo, a chimp. Jojo was off in a corner with her back turned to the psychologists. They noticed however that her shoulders appeared to be shaking. Then they noticed that she held a stick in one hand—and had her other hand clamped over her mouth. She was trying to muffle a guffaw.

Chimpanzees can laugh in genuinely human fashion and can even cry, but apparently cannot shed tears. They are also great ones for kissing and caressing and can become almost maudlin in their sympathy. One psychologist found he could get a chimp down out of a tree by pretending that he had hurt his arm. The chimp climbed down out of the tree, looked the arm over sympathetically and caressed it soothingly.

Another scientist working with chimps relates this

amazing incident. He drew his chair up before a cage containing an ape mother and infant. The mother clung to the infant tightly, and glared at the stranger scientist suspiciously. As the scientist picked up his chair to move closer to the cage, he got a large splinter in his finger.

He forgot the chimps as he began trying to extract the painful splinter. Suddenly he noticed that the mother had moved over closer and was staring sympathetically at the splinter. The man relates:

"The next instant—why I shall never understand— I gave her my hand. She clutched it and dipped my finger into her mouth. Then she set her thumbnail under the splinter and expertly flipped it out."

Most chimpanzees dote on medical attention, especially when they are ailing, and often reserve their greatest affection and appreciative attention for the human doctors who look after them.

Moos, a chimp at the Yerkes laboratories, complained vigorously about a toothache. The vet came and peered into Moos's enormous mouth. He saw nothing, and turned to walk away. Moos ran and grabbed the vet, pulled his simian mouth open with one finger, and pointed urgently toward an upper back corner with another finger. The vet looked again. Sure enough, way up in a far corner he saw the swelling of a tooth that hadn't come through yet.

A little chimpanzee at the St. Louis Zoo was losing one of his baby teeth. (Oh yes, chimps have baby teeth just as we do.) The tooth was loose and wobbled when the boy-chimp touched it with a finger, but it did not come out. And apparently it was causing him great pain. His comrades showed intense concern and sympathy for his plight. Several reached their ponderous fingers in his mouth and tried to pull the tooth loose, but they couldn't get a good hold.

Finally an attendant who happened to notice the commotion tossed a pair of pliers into the cage. After a few experiments the chimp succeeded in pulling the tooth. Then the whole crowd examined the tooth, hollered at it, bit it. One chimp threw it disdainfully on the floor and the crowd took turns jumping up and down on the nasty old tooth.

Outside the psychological laboratories, the place where the mental ability of chimpanzees has been most thoroughly tested is at the St. Louis Zoo. Here for many years chimps have been subjected to intensive training. The zoo's two dozen extra bright chimps have in fact been nicknamed the top Quiz Kids of animaldom.

If you have driven or strolled through St. Louis' spacious Forest Park, you may have seen the odd sight I saw when I was riding through the park in a cab. A midget car zipped up a side road. Its driver looked like any other person, he wore clothes like any other person, he drove like any other person, but technically he wasn't a person at all. He was a chimpanzee.

Chimpanzees at the St. Louis Zoo in Forest Park love to drive cars, indoors or out, and their accident record is better than that of the human drivers in St. Louis. Once when the chimps were pitted against four human drivers in a dodge-'em contest with their little battery-driven cars they proved decidedly superior in timing and accuracy as they careened around the arena, forward and backward, cool as daredevils. Unlike human drivers, the only times chimps have crack-ups is when they have been coached to do it, for laughs. This zoo's chimps were assembled there by the zoo's bouncy, cigar-chomping, hoarse-voiced director, George Vierheller.

Widely known as "The Barnum of zoo business" or "Mr. Zoo," George Vierheller in 40 years has built at St. Louis the most entertaining zoo the world has ever known. It is a place of joy and excitement where elephants play baseball, kangaroos box and lions frolic with humans.

Hospitably, Mr. Vierheller led me to a refreshment

stand and said, "Sambo, give Mr. Packard a sarsaparil-
la." Sambo, the attendant (who also happened to be a
chimp), promptly took out a bottle, removed the top
with a flick of his wrist, put two straws in the bottle and
handed it to me. Then Sambo leaped into Vierheller's
arms and they exchanged affectionate kisses and hugs.
The zoo-man estimates he has kissed his chimps about
5,000 times, and insists he enjoys it almost as much as
they do.

Sambo noticed that Vierheller's nine-cent cigar had
gone out, and indicated as much. Vierheller got out a
match. Sambo lit it, held it patiently while Vierheller
puffed his stogie into full blaze, then carefully blew out
the match. Meanwhile, I had not been able to finish my
soft drink. Vierheller handed it to Sambo, who sipped
some of it by straw. Vierheller said, "Aw, don't be a
sissy. Drink it man fashion." Sambo tossed away the
straws, threw back his head and downed the bottle's
contents in two gulps.

To show his gratitude he then leaped into my arms.
My fountain pen in the outside breast pocket of my
coat attracted his attention. He took out the pen, removed the cap, and looked around for some place to
write. I pulled out my notebook. Sambo laid it down on
the stand and dashed off a few cryptic notes. Vierheller,
peering over his shoulder, observed that Sambo's hand-
writing was just about as legible as mine.

People in St. Louis are delighted, but no longer surprised, to see animals from their zoo turn up in odd
places. Chimpanzees have strolled into a local Sears,
Roebuck store to be fitted for new suits. Vierheller has
been seen with a young elephant in his sedan driving
around the city. He frequently takes one of his chimp
pals along as a dinner companion when he goes to a
banquet that might otherwise prove dull.

When he returns from animal-buying trips to New
York, the Pennsylvania Railroad personnel have learned

to grin and bear it. Mr. V. may stride into the dining car with a chimp beside him and ask for a table for two. He protests that "it would break the animal's spirit" to be subjected to the indignity of making the trip in a crate.

But even Mr. Zoo was surprised by what happened when he found himself sharing a sleeping compartment with a chimp named Jackie. He had just purchased Jackie from a Long Island, New York, estate. Jackie wore fashionable tweeds, walked with a cane, sported a gold ring and was supposed to be unusually thoughtful, even for a chimp. When it came time to retire, Jackie refused to sleep anywhere except in the berth beside his new friend. In the middle of the night Mr. V. was awakened by the sound of something stirring. He quickly noted that he was alone in bed and that the compartment light was on. Then he heard water running in the bathroom toilet. Jackie came out of the bathroom, turned off the light, hopped into bed beside him, pulled up the covers and soon was snoring peacefully.

Vierheller buys his chimpanzees strictly on a trial basis. In two or three weeks he can tell if the chimp meets his stiff requirements: high intelligence; even, nonflighty temperament; affectionate, trusting nature; easy ability to walk upright and a touch of ham. Some chimps, he explained, are dull and humorless, just like some people. The chimps must be under ten years of age. Beyond that age (which is their puberty) they tend to become ornery and overbearing.

Persuading chimps to strut their stuff for human audiences requires a delicate combination of love and firmness. Seals will perform for fish, elephants for carrots, ponies for sugar. But with chimps bribes are not necessary. In fact, they're ill-advised. Chimps need only a pat on the back, and Vierheller comes around after every show to give it to them.

Another, and little-known, reason they do their best is

that they don't want to get in bad with their own chimp
boss. When you start building a show with ten chimps
there is no use even rehearsing until they fight and bluff
it out to see who is boss chimp, or Top Guy. When I
was there Roy was Top Guy, and would stand for no
monkey business. When little Peanuts began fooling
around and missed his cue to take a back-flip off a pony,
Roy blew his top—before 3,500 people—and began mop-
ping up the floor with Peanuts.

On stage the chimps always wear clothes, like anybody else. They have about a dozen costume changes
each—a total wardrobe of 130 get-ups. These are custom
made and donated by the Elder Manufacturing Company of St. Louis. The chimps don't particularly like
wearing clothes. In fact, if clothes are left on them when
they are put in their cages, they promptly tear them off.
They tolerate the clothes because Vierheller has seen to
it that they associate clothes with freedom. When Mr.
V. goes to Roy's cage and says, "Come on, Roy, let's go
for a car ride," Roy excitedly runs and get his clothes,
puts them on all by himself and races to the car. The
clothes have zippers. These fascinate the chimps so
much that with embarrassing frequency they start un-
zipping themselves in the middle of a performance—
which, of course, delights the audience.

Although the St. Louis chimps can learn to perform
just about any stunts their human trainers have been
able to conceive for them, their most impressive feats
are the things they do spontaneously, on their own. The
great chimp Nero, for example, was being taught to
walk a tightrope. One day, while standing at the wob-
bliest part of the rope, he decided he would add a little
zip to the act. He did a back somersault and landed upright—still on the rope! From then on Nero began doing
his show-stopping back-flip every day.

Another time, Nero was out driving the tiny Maxwell
around the zoo grounds when Vierheller suggested he

take one of Nero's lady fans (a corporation executive's wife) for a ride. The lady got into the back seat. Nero started the car so swiftly that she fell backward. Poor Nero was appalled. He rushed back and helped her from the ground. Graciously she got back into her seat. This time he started off very, very gently and kept looking back anxiously to see if she was still there.

The feat Mr. Zoo recalls most vividly, and painfully, occurred when several of his chimps were lodged in temporary cages at the monkey house while their own quarters at the special ape house were being overhauled. One day painters began redoing the walls near the chimp cages. The chimps watched in utter and envious fascination. Noon hour came and the painters went to lunch. Immediately the chimps began straining at the 36-inch wire of their temporary cages. Soon three had wiggled their way to freedom. They raced to the paint buckets, grabbed the brushes and started sloshing paint on the walls, on the floor and on each other. They were having a glorious time when they heard a furious shout. The building attendant was bearing down on them. They knew they had done wrong and were in trouble.

In a flash they dashed for the stairway leading to the office of their pal, Mr. Vierheller. He would protect them. At that moment, Mr. V. (nattily attired as usual) was starting down the stairs on his way to lunch at his club.

The three paint-sopped anthropoids leaped jabbering into his arms. For once Vierheller came mighty close to being angry with his impish chimps, but he finally decided philosophically, "In their place I guess I'd have done the same!"

Mr. Vierheller drove me out to the suburban home of his chief trainer Mike Kostial. Much of the training was being done at home because zoo officials had discovered that the young chimps especially, seemed to learn faster in the atmosphere of a human home. Mike Kostial, a slim, amiable man, greeted us at the door of his home, hammer in hand. He said he had been putting a guard over the light switch in the room where the chimps sleep to try to stop the chimp Duke from reaching through his cage and switching on the light at night. It was wasting electricity.

The scene at the Kostial home was typically domestic. Mrs. Kostial, a brunette, was washing dishes. In a high chair watching her was a diapered toddler named Tiny who was hugging a rubber toy. (Tiny is a toddler chimp.) In the living room the Kostials' six-year-old son Dennis and Duke the chimp were lounging in easy chairs watching TV. A cowboy picture was on. Mrs. Kostial explained: "I don't think Duke really cares much for TV, but he pretends to because he likes to be allowed out with people."

As we talked, Duke and Dennis began playing tag through the rooms. Mrs. Kostial scolded them. "Duke will take the house apart if I'm not strict with him," she said.

Now Duke had the refrigerator door open, reaching for a piece of cheese. It may startle zoologists (all the books say chimps are vegetarians), but Duke loves such human foods as fried chicken, hot dogs, catsup and cherry pie. However, Vierheller added, "If you offer him any of those human foods after we put him back in his cage at the zoo, he'll look at you like you are crazy."

Now Duke was put to "work," hiking around on low learner stilts. When Duke finished his stilt exercise, Kostial tossed him his football uniform, complete with headgear and shoulder pads. Duke zipped himself into his suit. Kostial handed him a football and in quarterback fashion said crisply, "Okay, hike! One, two, three, four . . ." Duke had bent down like a center, tossed the ball back between his legs to Kostial and then started running across the room. Kostial threw him a pass, which he caught easily. As I explained "Wow!" Duke whirled and rifled a lateral to me. The ball bounced off my chest. I felt foolish. Vierheller chuckled and said, "He was just seeing if you were good enough to make the team."

To keep his wonder zoo humming, Vierheller needs about half a million dollars a year. Less than two thirds of this comes from the people's zoo tax. (It amounts to about 38 cents a year per resident.) The rest is up to Vierheller's ingenuity. That's why Duke will be out at the refreshment stands occasionally promoting the sale of pop and postcards. Vierheller also raises about $10,000 each year by breeding animals and selling the offspring to private owners and to other zoos. Among private owners who want pets the greatest demand is for lion cubs, Barbary wild sheep, black buck antelope, tropical birds, and young chimps.

This past year Vierheller's zoo broke all the attendance records established during the 37 years since he received a political appointment to take charge of the city's then unimpressive collection of animal cages. He had been a telegrapher who lost his job, got into politics, and was given the obscure zoo post as a very minor political plum. St. Louis considers him its greatest booster in 100 years and has honored him with every award at its command. Recently the taxpayers showed their loyalty in a stern test. By a vote of 4 to 1 they increased their tax load so that he could have $1,625,000 to fulfill his dreams of expansion.

13.   The Shy, Misunderstood Gorilla

I T is about time, I believe, that somebody came to the defense of the gorilla, an outrageously defamed and maligned creature. The gorilla is a lot brighter, nicer animal than most of us realize.

The hoopla of circus and movie publicity experts about the monstrous limb-tearing savagery of gorillas has given the biggest of the apes a bad reputation. The maligning of the gorilla has penetrated so far that a presumably well-informed writer recently said that the gorilla "lives for one purpose—murder."

Actually the gorilla wouldn't deliberately hurt anyone except on extreme provocation. The New York Zoological Society is trying to clear up public misunderstanding about the gorilla. It states: "The name gorilla is wrongly used to express savagery and ferocity. In truth the gorilla is a normally peaceful citizen. It is a harmless vegetarian and attacks only when it or its family is attacked."

You may feel as if you are peering into the core of a volcano when you look into the sunken eyes of the ugly gorilla, and you may feel he is raring to tear you limb from limb when he beats his chest. Actually, he is just beating his chest because he's feeling particularly well. He can't help it that he happens to have the features of a monster.

Psychologists who have studied the gorilla have found

that it not only has a basically friendly nature but has surprisingly Man-like intelligence and emotions.

We have indicated in previous chapters that the chimpanzee is the champion quiz kid of the animal kingdom. On tests that psychologists have devised so far, the chimp stands supreme. The few gorillas that the scientists have managed to test have performed only moderately well. They were poor at mechanics and were slow in getting the idea of box-stacking. But their me-

MOTHER AND CHILD

A madonna of the jungle contentedly breast-feeds her baby, for all the world like her human counterpart.

diocre showing may be due to their shy, inhibited nature. They don't enjoy showing off as the exhibitionistic chimps do.

At any rate, scientists at the Yerkes Laboratories of Primate Biology concluded that the gorilla stands definitely closer to Man than the chimp in the structure of its nervous system, and nearer to Man in emotional stability. It has an inhibited manner and general aloofness which suggest the emotional restraint Man has achieved.

After spending many decades studying apes, the famed Dr. Yerkes concluded that the gorilla is ahead of the chimp in total psychological resemblances to Man, despite the fact that the chimp leads in intelligence tests.

The gorilla also has Man's passion for orderliness. When scientists at the Yerkes laboratories tested a gorilla named Congo on the problem of stacking boxes to reach suspended food, they noticed that while Congo was not so clever as the chimps in piling up boxes, she did stack her boxes neatly. The chimps, on the other hand, slapped their pyramids together helter-skelter.

When you give a gorilla a candy bar (which gorillas love) he will carefully unwrap the candy. After he has eaten the candy he will not throw the wrapper away but instead will crumple it up into the smallest possible pill and hide it in a corner.

Despite its limb-tearing reputation the gorilla is not destructive. If you give it a broom it will examine the strange object with great care, then set it aside. The chimp, in contrast, will soon have the broom torn to shreds.

This orderly tidiness of the gorilla shows up in many ways. When Congo was being tested, mechanical testing devices were set up outside her cage for her to operate. Part of her cage was in the open air but the room where she slept was sheltered. When she came out to face her testers one morning after a hard rain, she noticed that there was a puddle of water on the floor by the bars where she normally sat.

Congo looked at the puddle in indecision for a moment, then she came out again, and this time she carried an armful of dry straw from her couch. Carefully she scattered the straw over the puddle, then sat down and indicated she was ready to begin work.

Psychologists and attendants who work with adult gorillas stay out of arm's reach of their subjects not because the animals are vicious but because they fear they might be hugged to death in an affectionate embrace. Bushman, the huge gorilla with the strength of 30 men at Chicago's Lincoln Park Zoo, long had a jealous affection for a certain keeper. Bushman would sulk if his keeper attended to any other animals in sight first, but squealed with delight when he got first attention. The keeper never dared to go inside Bushman's cage for fear of getting a great big affectionate squeeze.

At New York's Bronx Zoo psychologists spent two hours a day for an entire summer sitting and taking notes in front of the twin cages of Oka (the shy, friendly female), and Makoko (the more muscular and aloof male gorilla). Neither one, the psychologists became convinced, had a mean disposition.

When Oka and Makoko were put together, the din that arose sounded as if they were trying to kill each other. Makoko would reach over, grab Oka by the hair and give it a tug. She would slap him. Then they would be off in an earth-shaking brawl. With their big bellies, they looked like over-aged professional wrestlers. Makoko would grab Oka by the crotch, lift her up and slap her to the floor. Oka would fly up at him. But whenever Oka screamed in pain, Makoko would quit, and look at her sympathetically. Both seemed to regard the wrestling as a pleasurable diversion.

Even when they were separated, Oka and Makoko could push food through the cage to each other. The

"IT'S A TEMPTING OFFER, OF COURSE,
BUT I'LL HAVE TO SLEEP ON IT."

Chimpanzees can learn to do almost anything a human being can do. Bozo, the phone-happy monkey in this photograph, not only listens in on the phone, but he loves to dial numbers.

psychologists noticed that Oka, the feminine flirt, was more apt to offer tidbits than was he-mannish Makoko.

Before gorillas became big enough to be dangerous, they often make charming, considerate companions. Quite a few years ago, according to the Bulletin of the New York Zoological Society, a scientific-minded maiden lady took a young 112-pound, five-year-old gorilla into her home as a house guest. The youngster was such a model that he was encouraged to remain for two years, as a member of the household.

This young gorilla was friendly, reasonably obedient, and almost always spotlessly clean. His extraordinary cleanliness resulted from the pleasure he got from taking showers. He learned to operate not only the shower but all the other bathroom facilities in the proper way.

At night he slept in a regular bed in his own room. If during the night he found it necessary to exercise the functions of elimination, he turned on the light in his room and went quietly to the bathroom. When he was ready to get back into bed again, he switched off the light, slipped into bed and carefully pulled the blankets up over himself.

In the jungle at night gorillas go to a great deal of bother to build themselves comfortable beds. Since they rove over wide areas (like nomad humans) they have to build a new bed every night. They break off branches of trees and pile them up into luxurious, springy piles, and sometimes tie knots in the tops of young saplings and bend them down to form a sort of hammock. The psychologist Dr. James Bender reports that naturalists have found as many as *24 complete knots and ties* in the saplings that make up a gorilla bed.

Gorillas, incidentally, are tremendous snorers. A leading authority on the gorilla's jungle habits is A. I. Good, a naturalist and missionary who has spent more than 35 years in the jungles of French Cameroun, West Africa, which is real "gorilla country." Mr. Good was collecting animals and insects for leading U. S. museums. He related that the gorilla apparently makes a loud terrifying noise while sleeping.

One night Mr. Good listened to a weird sound which natives assured him was a gorilla's snoring. He reported to the American Museum of Natural History's *Animal Kingdom:* "I heard a voice like the syllables, 'bup-bup-bup-bup-bup-bup' repeated rapidly. It began rather low, rising to a cresendo and dying down again. . . . It sounded at least a half mile away. The natives believe that this snoring must give some measure of protection to the sleeping gorilla, as nothing would attack an animal that made noises like that."

In the jungle gorillas rarely attack a human being without provocation. Where the gorillas are common, the natives do not consider them a serious threat. (And the gorillas apparently do not consider the human natives a serious threat.)

When a native and a gorilla encounter each other, there is usually a good deal of hollering back and forth. Mr. Good related: "Occasionally a big male gorilla will make a pretense of attacking, but that is a bluff. He will approach to perhaps 20 or 30 feet, act threateningly, roar fiercely, stamp on the ground, turn his rear on you in a disgusting manner while watching you over his shoulder but will not push the attack home if you stand up to him. He does not like to have you around and evidently wants to scare you off his premises."

From centuries of experience natives have learned that if you come upon a gorilla and he roars menacingly at you, you should roar back at him.

Mr. Good one afternoon had his own chilling face-to-face encounter with a Gargantua-like monster in the gorilla-infested jungle near Metet. He strayed down a long jungle path after butterflies until he came to a little clearing. He was so deeply intent on capturing some Lycaenidae or Little Blues that only gradually did he become aware that someone was coming down the narrow path toward him. He looked. His eyes froze. A tremendous swaying gorilla was bearing down on him. It was only 20 yards away.

Mr. Good was armed only with his butterfly net, his tweezers and his insect bottle. He admits now that he was petrified with fright. What should he do? His impulse was to run, but natives had warned him:

"Whatever you do, don't run. If you do, the gorilla will certainly chase you, and being at home in his own forest, he will catch you. Stand up to him, and play the man."

So Mr. Good decided to be a Menace. He waved his butterfly net vigorously over his head. He relates:

"The gorilla seemed much interested in this new development. Monkey-like, he cocked his head to one side, then to the other to get a better look—and came down the path."

In addition to waving the net wildly, Mr. Good now began shouting in the deepest roar he could muster. When the gorilla was 18 yards away (Mr. Good measured the distance later) it came to a stop. For a long moment the gorilla looked this noisy, arm-waving man up and down, then stepped into the bush calmly and moved gradually away, eating berries as it went. When the gorilla was several feet from the path, the elderly Mr. Good dashed away. He sprinted down the narrow path, hurdled a log three feet above the path, tumbled as he landed on the other side, turned a complete somersault—and kept on running back to camp. He was still panting from excitement and exhaustion an hour later.

The conflict between gorilla and Man, in gorilla country, comes largely over Man's banana groves. Gorillas have great fondness not only for bananas but for tender banana shoots. A couple of hungry gorillas can make a shambles of a big grove in a single night. Since firearms are prohibited to practically all natives, they depend on noise to keep gorillas away at night. They post sentries who beat furiously on pans and drums periodically during the night.

In some areas the natives erect gorilla "scarecrows" to keep the giant apes away. Usually they used a stuffed effigy of a man. But they find this "scare-gorilla" works only for a couple of days, then its position and appearance must be changed or the lurking gorillas become suspicious of the fraud.

Natives do not hesitate to travel alone through long

stretches of the jungle unarmed, if they have a bicycle. They have found that the sudden squawk of its horn will scare off any gorilla that may stand on the path.

Scientists have been intrigued by Mr. Good's report that the Bulu people of southern Cameroun maintain that there is a third Great Ape in the equatorial African jungle that is unknown in scientific literature. Natives of the jungle know well every animal that moves and they insist there is an ape-like creature in the jungle that is neither gorilla nor chimpanzee, but a cross between them, and very big.

The natives even have a distinct name in their language for the animal. In the Bulu language the gorilla is called *ngi*, the chimpanzee is called *woc,* and this third mysterious creature is called *ebot*. Perhaps an *ebot* doesn't really exist, but you would have a hard time convincing a Bulu native of that.

14. Animals that Learned to Love Money

UNQUESTIONABLY animals are capable of some remarkable feats of intelligence. For example, we've seen animals escaping from Houdini contraptions . . . tying knots . . . plotting ambushes . . . counting and telling time . . . sawing wood . . . playing jokes . . . stacking boxes . . . and outshining children on IQ tests.

Often animals have proven to be startlingly clever. But still many of us have assumed that there is a definite, rigid ceiling to animal intelligence. Many psychologists have long held this view. They say there is a vast gulf separating the brightest animal and the dumbest Man. That gulf is based mainly on Man's ability to use *symbols*.

Much of human behavior that elevates us above the animal level is based on symbols. We use them entirely, for example, when we talk. Our words, whether we speak them or write them, are symbols. Most of us can't even think without forming our thoughts with these word-symbols.

Another excellent example of our use of symbols is the money we exchange for goods of real value. A dollar bill is a piece of paper worthless in itself, yet we treasure it because of its symbol value. We know we can swap it for a piece of steak or a box of candy.

Scientists have long assumed that the use of symbols is an exclusively human talent. In recent years, however, their belief has been shaken by some fascinating experiments. Certain animals, it now appears, cannot only understand the symbolism of money—they can become positively mad about money.

The experimenters have found that a few brainy animals can readily develop into shrewd, crafty, greedy capitalists who will work hard to gain an honest or crooked dollar.

In experiments at Columbia University it was discovered that even white rats can be taught to trade marbles for food. With the rats, however, the trading appears to be more a matter of conditioned learning than of getting them to regard marbles as money-symbols worth treasuring.

Psychologists have been vastly more impressed by a cebus monkey named Trader who lived at the San Diego Zoo. Quite spontaneously Trader had developed the strategy of winning peanuts and candy from spectators by offering to swap bits of his own ration which he didn't regard as very appetizing.

He would hold up pieces of his own food and chatter his willingness to swap. People in San Diego thought this was cute and began coming from miles around to swap stuff with Trader. Soon Trader found he could win food by offering practically anything, a pebble, a stick or a picking from his nose.

He was riding high, and in danger of dying of gluttony, when a psychologist heard of his feats, bought him and took him to the controlled economy of a laboratory. This was all right with Trader. When the psychologist would extend his hand and say "Trader, give me something," Trader would trot around until he found a piece of paper or door stop and bring it to the psychologist. If that didn't win any food in return, he would hunt up something else. If, however, after giving the psychologist four or five different items a swap was still not forthcoming, Trader would throw a fit all over the place and holler that he was being exploited.

The psychologist tried another approach. He put boxes containing different-colored poker chips in various places in the room. Each time Trader brought a white chip he was given a banana. A blue chip netted him a peanut, a red chip a piece of orange and a green chip a slice of bread. Finally there was a box of yellow chips, which—it developed—were worth nothing at all.

Trader soon began bringing white chips more than any other kind, to win the banana which was his favorite food. Next to the white chips, he brought more blue chips than any other. This was significant, because next to the banana there was nothing Trader liked better than peanuts.

Only rarely did he offer the worthless chips or the green bread chips. Trader considered bread a contemptible excuse for food.

He did occasionally bring the green (bread) chips and the worthless yellow chips, but only after he had first eaten his fill of bananas and peanuts. This fact has particularly fascinated psychologists. Yale's Professor Frank Beach, describing, in *Animal Kingdom,* experiments that have been made on animals with money had this to say:

"It seems to me that only one explanation fits the facts. In Trader's veins there must have coursed a bit of Yankee blood. Even when he made no profit on the transaction, he tried to promote a trade just for the sake of making a deal."

This swapping of chips for edibles was as far as the monkey Trader advanced in the financial world, but six young chimpanzees, in a classic experiment at Yale, had proved capable of mastering an even more subtle, Manlike economy.

At the Yale Laboratories of Primate Biology Dr. John Wolfe first introduced his chimps to a special slot machine, called the "Chimp-O-Mat," which would yield up one grape when a white poker chip was inserted in the slot.

The only way an animal could conceivably learn to operate the slot machine was by imitating human instructors, because the odds were a million to one that the operation could not be learned by trial and error. We have shown that with most animals, such as dogs, it has been utterly impossible to get them to learn anything by imitation. Yet the brainy chimps readily imitated their instructor. For example, when Dr. Wolfe showed a young chimp named Moos how he could win himself a grape by inserting a chip, Moos immediately picked up another chip, pushed it awkwardly into the slot, then stuck his ponderous paddy into the cup and waited eagerly for a grape to drop out.

At the beginning of the experiments the six chimps had shown little interest in poker chips. Chips were inferior playthings. But when the chimps learned that the chips could be used to make that funny machine disgorge grapes, they began treasuring the chips and fighting over them.

In addition to the white chips the chimps were given brass slugs. The slugs could be thrust into the slot, but nothing ever came out. In short, the slugs were worthless, and the chimps soon comprehended that fact. When a handful of white chips and brass slugs was tossed into the cage housing Bula, Bimba and Alpha, the three girl-chimps scrambled like human lady gold-diggers for the white chips, but never touched the brass slugs. The slugs were scorned as worthless.

After the chimps had all learned to operate the slot machine, Dr. Wolfe adjusted it so that the grape would not drop out until several minutes after a chip had been inserted. This proved infuriating in the extreme to the customers. Moos would insert the coin, then put his hand in the cup. When no grape dropped out he shook the machine violently. In the words of Dr. Beach:

"Moos looked like a frustrated subway customer who has wasted a penny in a defective gum machine."

By now our once-innocent apes were madly in love with money, and the pleasures that come from its acquisition. But would they work for it? That was the question that intrigued the psychologists, especially since Man has had little success in domesticating apes to menial labor. No animal had ever worked hard for wages, in the sense that men work for wages. Would the apes do so?

The real value of money—according to economists—is the amount of effort an individual will expend to acquire it. Did the six chimps value money enough to hustle for it?

To find the answer, Dr. Wolfe constructed a fiendishly clever device called the Work Machine. The chimps were shown that when a large handle was lifted, they could reach in and pick up one grape. When they learned the knack of lifting the handle to get the grape Dr. Wolfe pulled a switcheroo on them. Instead of the grape they would find one poker chip. This chip would still buy them one grape at the Chimp-O-Mat.

Thus the complexity of getting a grape was not only doubled, but the money to buy the grape could be obtained in no way except by honest sweat. You see, the handle of the Work Machine they had to lift to get the chip weighed 18 pounds. It takes real grunting and sustained effort for a young chimp to hoist that burden.

Yet the formerly indolent chimps not only quickly

SPENDING HIS HARD-EARNED "MONEY"

This chimpanzee at the Yale Laboratories of Comparative Psychobiology learned about "money" by dropping a chip into the coin machine. A grape dropped out. Soon he was a very money-mad monkey.

mastered the new, enlarged operation, but demonstrated their feverish eagerness to work for money.

Moos and Bimba worked at such a frenzied pace to
acquire chips, when given unlimited access to the Work
Machine, that the attendants soon began fearing for
their health. They amassed great piles of poker chips,
and guarded their piles with a ferocity new to the
chimps.

In one brief 10-minute period, Moos hoisted that
heavy handle 185 times. That was the equivalent of lifting 3,300 pounds. He was in such a rush to earn money

that he didn't even pick up each chip as he lifted the handle, but instead brushed it to the floor where a pile was growing.

Gradually, however, Moos developed restraint. He only worked hard when he was low on chips and felt hungry for grapes. When he had a large backlog of chips, he viewed the Work Machine with only mild interest. Likewise if the psychologist would give him, absolutely free, a pile of chips before bringing out the Work Machine, Moos would hoist the handle only a few times before quitting. However, if Moos was dead broke when the Work Machine was brought out, he would invariably hoist the handle energetically at least 100 times before quitting. Here is how Professor Beach interprets Moos's behavior:

"Like many human beings the chimpanzee's willingness to exert himself for pay depends in large measure on the current state of his financial reserves."

When a human worker earns a dollar, he doesn't run right out and spend it on ice cream or shoes. He lets the money accumulate for a week and then gets it all in a weekly paycheck. (Some human workers can even wait two weeks or a month before getting and spending their money.)

Could our six chimps show some such self-control in waiting to spend their hard-earned money? Some could not. Velt, for example, wanted to cash in his chips the minute he earned them by running to the Chimp-O-Mat. If the Chimp-O-Mat wasn't available, the chips burned holes in his pocket and he soon lost interest in working. Moos and Bimba, on the other hand, proved themselves capable of real thrift. They were quite willing to sweat at the Work Machine earning chips even though they couldn't spend their money until the following day.

When the Work Machine was mastered by all six chimps, Dr. Wolfe introduced a further Man-like refinement to the laboratory's economy. The brass slug was still worthless and the white poker chip was worth one grape. But when a blue chip was inserted into the Chimp-O-Mat, two grapes dropped out. A red chip inserted brought a drink of water. And a yellow chip, when inserted in a slot by the door of the testing room, brought the chimp a piggy-back ride on the psychologist's shoulders back to his own living quarters.

It takes a pretty high level of intelligence to comprehend that coins have different values. For example, if a typical pre-school human youngster asks for a dime and you give him a nickel, he is quite pleased. He still doesn't quite comprehend that a dime will buy more than a nickel. If he comprehends anything, it is that the nickel is bigger than the dime and thus is presumably worth more.

Our chimps, however, soon showed their awareness that blue chips were more valuable than white chips. The once-treasured white chips were now passed up in favor of the blue (two grape) chips when both were available. If the chimps were deprived of water until they were thirsty, they always chose red (water) chips over either the blue or white ones.

As for the yellow chips, their value was demonstrated dramatically by Bula. One afternoon, as Bula was happily standing by the Chimp-O-Mat inserting her blue chips, Dr. Wolfe walked up near her, opened a box and placed a white rat on the floor near Bula.

Lady chimps are as appalled by rats as are human ladies. When Bula saw the rat she stood aghast. Where could she flee? She looked around desperately—and began sidling away from the horrible beast. Suddenly she ran over to the box of yellow chips, inserted one in the slot by the door, then took a flying leap up onto the psychologist's shoulder and chattered frantically for him to take her out of there!

The seamy side of money was soon apparent as the

chimpanzees became accustomed to a money economy. The corrupting effects of greed set in. Once-friendly chimps became covetous or suspicious of neighbors. Subtle bullying became rampant.

Bula, for example, began lording it over Bimba. When they were lodged together and a large supply of chips was placed at their disposal, Bula took charge of almost all the chips and left the more submissive Bimba with only odds and ends. When the Chimp-O-Mat was rolled up to their cage, both rushed to spend their money, but Bula shouldered Bimba aside and began spending her huge pile on the orange slices that were on the menu that day. As Bula sucked one orange slice after another, Bimba whined for a chance to get at the machine. Instead of moving aside, Bula began handing poor Bimba the peels she had sucked dry.

All these experiments were highly entertaining. But to psychologists their significance is this: they prove that chimpanzees, and to a lesser extent the more primitive cebus monkeys, can comprehend symbols that represent food, water, and even piggy-back rides. Since symbols are necessary tools to intelligent, Man-like thinking, it would appear that the chimps have at least the basic tools for rudimentary thinking.

15. Do Animals Chat—or Chatter?

THE great gulf between Man and beast is said to center mainly around Man's ability to employ a language for communication. We talk in symbols. Each word we use represents things, actions, events, etc. These word-symbols are the raw materials we use to build thoughts. Language has helped Man become known as "the thinking animal."

We know, of course, that no other animal has a printed language with ABC's and dictionaries and rules of grammar. But do any animals in the world possess a means of communication that would pass as a language?

First we should note that the gulf between Man and beast with regard to language is not so vast as we once believed. One philologist has said that the orangutan "stands on the very threshold of human speech." And we must remember that certain human beings on this planet could never qualify as Rhodes scholars. Some Bushmen, for example, are unable to talk after dark. Why? Because much of their "language" depends on gestures and grimaces as aids to spoken words.

Many fanciful people have contended that the birds and the bees and almost all other creatures have a "language" of their own. Let us take a look through the animal kingdom for evidences of communication that can stand up as language.

Even fish talk, it has been discovered. Shrimps snap,

toadfish coo, gurnards grunt. Many fish noises were discovered in wartime research on undersea listening devices. It was found that some fish "talked" so noisily that they masked the sound of propellers. The noises fish make, however, appear to have very little connection with language. Scientists who have watched fish making noises have observed that they never answer each other.

In 1960 famed neuro-physiologist Dr. John Lilly was reported convinced, after years of study, that dolphins could perhaps be taught to talk, and he set out on a project to try to teach them. The playful dolphins are not fish as many assume but rather are mammals. And they have brains proportionately the size of man's. They also have well-developed vocal cords. He found one day during experiments that the dolphins apparently were mimicking his speech.

Every child knows, of course, that parrots can say "Polly wants a cracker," and "Help, get me out of here!" It is not widely known, but several other birds are almost as talented as the parrot in imitating sounds produced by human beings. Bullfinches have been taught to whistle musical airs. Starlings can toss off short sentences almost as competently as parrots, and crows have been taught to say words. The mocking bird readily reproduces the songs of other birds. And several different birds have been heard barking like dogs.

All these instances, however, are feats of mimicry; they are not evidences of language. Occasionally, it is true, the parrot pipes "Hello" when someone enters the room, but that can be accounted for as an example of simple association, just as it yells in happy excitement whenever its mistress enters with food.

Still, we don't have to go far among animals to find unmistakable evidences of communication. The rabbit thumps its hind feet to convey anger. The elephant trumpets its alarm. And all beavers scurry for cover when a beaver sentry slaps his heavy tail against the water. In fact, almost every animal mother in the wilds can cue its young to freeze motionless close to the ground. A hen may do this with a cluck and the doe with a soft bleat. It apparently is instinctive for wild youngsters to unquestioningly obey cues from the mother. The instinct was necessary for survival.

The tail of a White-Tail or Virginia Deer is a foot long. When held close to the body it shows only dull brown that blends with the forest. But when the tail is raised it shows a flash of white. As a doe goes through the forest she examines clump after clump of bushes and every path-crossing for possible enemies. If the coast is clear she raises her white tail flag for an instant and the fawn (or sometimes the entire herd) comes forward from hiding to join her.

Dog-owners know that their dog utters a wide range of meaningful sounds. A dog in its bark can express surprise, pleasure, pleading, alarm, playfulness.

In laboratories, raccoons succeed to an amazing degree in informing their human nurses as to their wants, as well as to the things they don't like. They have angry growls, contented gurgles, impatient hollerings.

Much of the noise made by male animals of many species is their mating call, or their warning to other males that they have laid claim to the particular territory where they stand, so lay off! The Department of Animal Behavior of the American Museum of Natural History has recordings made of the bellowing of a bull alligator. Psychologists took this record very close to a spot where another bull alligator was dozing in a pool. While the recording was being played the bull alligator in the pool suddenly began thrashing about full of fight and bellowing his roaring warning that he was king of his particular spot.

Many different scientists, especially German scientists, have spent months and years listening to different dumb creatures for evidences of language. One professor recorded seven words among roosters. . . . Another scientist studying horses distinguished six words and three kinds of neighing. . . . And still another man recorded 15 words among domestic cats.

Scientists have noted that domesticated animals have learned a form of communication not known to their wild brothers. That is the art of begging. A cat has a peculiar meow to let you know it would like food, and a dog has an urgent whine to let you know it wants to come indoors. In the wilds the animals don't have a master and so have no need to beg. Faced with an abnormal situation, domesticated animals have had to improvise.

When a roving ant or bee comes across a rich stockpile of food, it hurries excitedly back home. Soon a whole swarm of ants or bees is hustling straight toward the discovered food even though it may be a great distance away and even though the discoverer does not accompany them. How do these insects know where to go? Do insects have a language? This has been one of the great mysteries of Nature. Many scientists have tried to solve it. Pretty good evidence is now in on both the ants and the bees.

When a food-finding ant returns to its nest and meets another ant, there is usually an excited and rapid exchange of antennal taps. Some imaginative writers have stated that these taps convey specific, precise information on the whereabouts of the discovered food. Today the prevailing opinion of such ant authorities as Schneirla is that the finder merely communicates his excitement. He dashes about exchanging taps with every ant he can find.

But how do the ants at the nest know where to go? This mystery was solved by investigators who found that when members of many ant species become excited by the discovery of food their anal glands release a stronglyodored substance that forms a trail. This odor trail leads from the discovered food directly to the nest.

One investigator confirmed that other ants follow this trail when he set up a laboratory situation in which the floor between food and the nest was covered with paper. After the ant that discovered the food raced excitedly back into the nest, the scientist quickly substituted fresh paper for the original paper containing the odor trail. As the ants swarmed out in excitement they went sniffing helter-skelter in search of a trail. Soon they were widely dispersed, and the few that found the food did so only by chance.

With bees, however, trail-laying is out of the question because they fly through the air. The problem with bees is also complicated by the fact that they forage out to distances up to two miles for nectar. Thus, precise information is needed if other bees are to find a particular nectar-loaded flower.

How is the information conveyed? One Austrian zoologist, Karl von Frisch, spent 40 years trying to solve this puzzle. He held a professorship at Munich and was in danger of being ousted by the Nazis, but his study of bees was considered so important by the German food ministry that his removal was postponed until after the war. Later he established his own private laboratory in the Austrian Alps.

Von Frisch constructed special hives with a glass plate for viewing activities inside the hive. He soon found that food-finding bees went into an odd dance upon returning to the hive. Gradually he noticed that the dancing took two distinct forms. One was a circling dance, the other was a wagging dance during the course of which the bee runs in a straight line a certain distance, wags its belly very swiftly, then makes a turn.

This dance excites the other bees. They begin imitating it, then go zooming out on a beeline for the discovered nectar. They apparently know what flower to look for because of the odor that sticks to the body of the nectar-finding bee.

But what was the significance of the two dances? Von Frisch discovered this by training two sets of bees in the same hive to feed in two different areas. One set marked with a blue stain was trained to feed at a spot only a few yards away, whereas red-stained bees fed at a spot nearly a quarter of a mile away. Prof. von Frisch himself danced with delight as he observed his bees dancing. All the blue bees did circling dances, and all the red bees from the far-away spot performed wagging dances.

To double-check his discovery, von Frisch pulled a switcheroo on his bees. Gradually he moved the blue bees' feeding place further away and brought the red bees closer to home. At a zone roughly 100 yards away, the blue bees began switching from their circling dance to a wagging dance, and the red bees began switching from a wagging to a circling dance.

So far, then, we find that the bees know what kind of flower the discovered nectar is in and whether it is more or less than 100 yards away. But is that all the clues they have? Von Frisch decided there must be more, so he kept watching. More years passed. Gradually he noticed that in the wagging (long-distance) dance some bees made many more turns in a 15-second period than others. Following up this lead, he found that a bee returning from a spot 100 yards or so away would make ten short turns in 15 seconds, whereas the bee returning from two miles away would make only three turns in 15 seconds. Thus the bees were apparently given fairly definite information on the distance to the nectar.

But what direction would the bees go to find the food? They obviously did know what point on the compass to set out for, but how did they know? This mystery occupied von Frisch for still more years. His first key was the discovery that bees use the sun to orient themselves during flight. Later he found that the finder-bee revealed the direction of the food by the direction towards which it danced on the hive. If the food was straight toward the sun, the dancing bee danced straight up the vertical side of the hive, with its head *up*. If the food was in the direction away from the sun it danced in the same direction but with its head *down*. If the food was 45 degrees to the right of the sun, the bee danced in a direction 45 degrees away from straight up the hive.

Here we unmistakably have clear communication. We even have the use of symbols in the form of dancing. Thus bee communication should qualify as a rudimentary language even though not a word is spoken and it is all done instinctively.

If any animals have a highly developed spoken "language," we would expect to find it in the primates because they are closest to Man on the evolutionary scale, and in tests have revealed themselves to be the brightest boys of the animal kingdom.

Differences within the monkey family itself are significant. Lemurs are the most primitive and dull-witted monkeys. In fact they barely qualify as monkeys. They chatter, scream, squawk and grunt all day and night. On the other hand, orangutans and chimpanzees, both Great Apes who are closest to Man in intelligence, are wise and gifted linguists. They don't gibber. Instead, they talk tersely and to the point.

An early associate of Robert Yerkes, the noted ape authority, compiled a dictionary of chimpanzee words. This investigator, Blanche W. Learned, was able to distinguish 32 different chimpanzee words. Most of the words were associated with food or drink or with other animals or persons.

One philologist, George Schwidetzky, even wrote a book called *Do You Speak Chimpanzee?* He found that the chimpanzee word for "Hello" is a kind of oo-oo-oo bark. This greeting, he discovered, immediately evokes a friendly response from other chimpanzees that hear it.

To test out the word Mr. Schwidetzky went to the London Zoo and approached the chimpanzee cage. He said "Hello" to them in English. The chimps glanced at him casually and, seeing that he had no food, went back to their blackhead-pinching. Mr. Schwidetzky walked away and returned a few moments later. This time he said "Hello" to them in chimpanzee.

The result was electrifying. Several returned the greeting, and all the chimpanzees in the cage rushed over to the railing and allowed the man to tickle and scratch them as if they were old friends. Mr. Schwidetzky said:

"One even showed me a hole in the wire where I could catch hold of his hand and shake it."

Linguists have claimed to find actual language "bridges" between chimpanzee words and human words in common use today. The philologist George Schwidetzky states, for example, that the Bushmen of South Africa have a tongue click similar to the chimpanzee's, and that the "ngak" sound frequently used by chimps is "splendidly preserved" in ancient Chinese. Also he mentions that the chimp word "gack" still survives in German as "geck," meaning dandy.

The chimp, he believes, would have little difficulty pronouncing our words "nag," "neck," "neigh" and "knack." (Another expert has suggested that if only the chimp could speak English he would do so with "a slight brogue.") As to the question, "Do chimpanzees have a language?" Schwidetzky says the answer depends on what you mean by language. If you mean communicating what is felt, willed and thought, then the answer is "yes." But if you mean can the chimp express a chain of logical thought, then the answer unquestionably is "no." The chimp has no grammar. Neither the chimp nor any other animal has ever mastered a true language.

Scientists have also found that the gibbon, a small

BULL SESSION

These four lads look as if they might have been discussing the latest stock-market reports. Although their vocabulary is limited, it's likely that they have no trouble communicating with each other.

monkey-like ape, has a fairly extensive vocabulary. When it is pleased about something it cries, "Hok hug hug, hag kuag, guaggak."

An American investigator studying orangutans taught one little female to say "papa," meaning the investigator, and to say "cup" when she was thirsty. The little orang seemed to have some conception of the meaning of the words. One day when she was ill and her throat was parched, she leaned out of her hammock and called "Cup, cup, cup." When water was brought, she drank it greedily.

If the man asked her "Where is papa?" the orang would come and lay her hand on his shoulder. One hot day when she was near a pool, she slipped on the edge of the pool and her legs got wet, which terrified her. She ran to the investigator calling "Papa, papa, papa," and flung her arms around his neck.

Gorillas under investigation have exhibited little perceptible skill at language, but natives of gorilla-land have an interesting belief. They are convinced that gorillas talk just as well as you and I when they are by themselves in the jungle, but that they carefully conceal their talking talents when human beings are around.

Why are they mum around humans? They're mum, the natives believe, because they know that if men catch them talking, they will be drafted into the labor battalions where human natives have to serve, and would be forced to pay taxes! This evasion of the labor draft and of paying taxes by the Man-like gorillas causes some bitterness among the hard-working, tax-paying human natives of the jungle.

That, as we say, is an interesting theory. But until it is proven we are left with the evidence at hand. That is that several animals, particularly the apes, have the rudiments of human speech and can express their feelings with some eloquence but are incapable of making conversation. A dog can let you know he likes or dislikes a bone very much, but there is no evidence he can say anything *about* the bone even to other dogs beyond "mmmmmm" or "bah." He can't say that the flavor reminds him of rabbit or that he would like it better if it were a ham hock instead of pig's knuckle.

16. Some Strange Devotions

MOTHER love in all mammals is a passionate, unreasoning thing. Among mammals the responsibility for nurturing, protecting and rearing the young falls almost entirely on the mother. The result is that Nature has implanted in these wild mothers a profound impulse to nurture infants.

The impulse is so strong that wild mothers occasionally show little discrimination between their own offspring and the young on an entirely different species. A mother cat that has lost her kittens will go out and kidnap baby rabbits and nurse them herself.

Cat mothers, in fact, have turned up with some weird assortments of creatures as wards. Probably this is because cat mothers are so often frustrated in their motherhood by callous human masters who drown their kittens. A mother cat may have three litters, or perhaps 15 or 20 kittens in a year. Few people today want that many cats cluttering up their homes, so they drown the newborn kittens or give them away. A picture magazine recently printed photos of four different mother cats that had taken on strange boarders.

—A sleek black mother cat in Chicago's suburbs went out and found herself two baby rabbits when she lost four of her own five babies.

—A white cat in Grove, Oklahoma, adopted a week-old ground hog which her owner, a Cherokee Indian, found on a hunting trip. When she happened to see the ground hog in a box, she picked it up by the nape of the neck and lugged it to her retreat in the barn.

—A tiger cat in LaMesa, California, adopted three baby skunks.

—A black, long-haired mother cat in Nevada City, California, who already had four kittens, cheerfully added two baby squirrels to her litter.

There's always room for a couple more mouths! The milk of cats is rich, and suitable for all sorts of mammals. In the case of this last mother who had both kittens and squirrels, the mother, interestingly enough, was completely impartial. The young squirrels, being huskier, tended to elbow the kittens aside in the competition to get to the choice feeding stations. The mother raised no objection.

At Bear Mountain State Park officials of one of the camps have reported what happened in the case of a mother cat that had lost all her kittens. One day in her prowling she came upon a litter of infant raccoons in a box. Their mother had apparently been killed.

The mother cat walked into the box where the baby raccoons were and looked them over curiously. One of the coons whimpered. The cat tenderly licked its face. Then she stepped carefully to the center of the mass of squirming coons, moved several aside with her paw, and laid herself down. The hungry little coons began swarming over her. Soon every one of them had found a teat yielding nourishment.

Several cases have been reported where dogs have also mothered some strange creatures. In Lufkin, Texas, a fawn was found almost dead from hunger. The man finding the fawn tried to feed it cow's milk, but that proved indigestible. Then, as a desperate last resort, he took the fawn to the kennel where a hound bitch was nursing her pup. The fawn readily joined in the feast, and in a few days was back in good health.

In St. Petersburg, Florida, a Scottie was deprived of her litter of ten pups. She disappeared into the woods. A few hours later she returned lugging a baby raccoon so small that its black mask and the rings on its tail were barely perceptible. Then she went back into the woods. By the end of the afternoon she had commandeered three baby raccoons.

There are likewise many authentic cases of grown dogs having strange cronies. A man in Texas reared two young wolves. They romped very amiably with neighboring dogs.

There have even been cases of breeding between wolves and domestic dogs. A fox in Michigan, for example, used to come out of the woods every day and play with a young fox terrier.

In Yakima, Washington, a cocker spaniel named Rusty and a pet duck named Donald became inseparable pals. Donald waddled after Rusty wherever he went, shared his food and his bed. The duck, being reared in isolation from other ducks, developed for some reason a dread of water. The dog in contrast loved water and often gave the duck a ride on his back.

The skunk, in the wilds, is usually shunned by other creatures for good and sufficient reason. But when thrown into contact with other animals in captivity, it proves itself to be a delightful and appreciative companion.

At Bear Mountain State Park a skunk and coon became inseparable friends and staged a wrestling match every afternoon. The coon would even playfully try to pull the skunk's tail, perhaps to show what a daredevil he was. The two were separated permanently when their romps became too rough. This action grieved the coon very much. He began snapping at the man who had separated them, and never forgave him.

One of the strangest reported adoptions was that of a family of baby skunks that was taken under the wing of a hen. It wasn't the hen's idea. She was setting peaceably on her own eggs when a boy on the farm found a litter of baby skunks whose mother had been killed by his dog.

The boy felt guilty, and responsible for the infant skunks' survival. He began feeding the blind little striped infants with a medicine dropper. And to keep them warm between feedings he shoved them under the setting hen.

Soon the hen began pecking at the boy when he came near. She had become very proud of her furry brood and somehow decided they were her own children.

A LITTLE GIRL AND HER DOLL

Oka is now a gigantic gorilla at New York's Bronx Zoo, but when this picture was made she was still a little girl and loved to play with her monkey-faced doll. Now, full-grown and ferocious-looking, she remains shy and affectionate, and like any other gorilla wouldn't deliberately hurt a soul.

When the skunks opened their eyes and were able to move about, they followed the strutting hen wherever she went. As the young skunks became bigger, trouble developed because they were playful and the hen, like all winged creatures, had an extremely limited sense of humor. The skunks' playful nips finally became too much for her and she walked out on them. But by then they were just about ready to take care of themselves, anyhow.

Many birds seem to follow their mother or any adult bird that takes care of them, instinctively. In several experiments human beings have had little difficulty getting infant birds to regard them as "mother."

A German biologist, Dr. Konrad Lorenz, robbed a goose of her eggs just before they hatched and saw to it that he was the first moving creature the newborn birds beheld after they emerged from their shells. He looked after them and was careful to reward them with food whenever he called them.

Soon he had the little goslings tagging him in single file wherever he went. He walked much faster than the goslings could normally travel, but they trotted clumsily behind him and seemed terrified when they fell behind. When he got into a canoe and began paddling across a lake, the goslings hopped into the water and took out after him single file. Finally, when they were able to fly he tried them out on his supreme test. He climbed into a small airplane which took him soaring into the sky. He looked back. The goslings were flopping through the air, trying desperately to keep up with the plane. By this time possibly they were cursing the inconsiderateness of their "mother."

ODD PAIR

This cub seems merely curious but actually he is well on his way to making a friend of this graceful fawn.

Evidently it is not a sense of love or devotion that makes the young tag after the mother and stay close to her. Instead, it is a sense of dependence, a deep desire to be protected and guided. Robert Briffault states:

"All young animals will attach themselves to the first creature, animal or human, that will look after them. Newborn chicks will follow any moving object."

He mentions reports that when Indians used to kill cow buffalo, the calf would follow the Indians and lick their fingers. Likewise the young offspring of a rhinoceros, when its mother is shot by hunters, will trot along quietly after the human slayers of its own mother, and follow the men right into their camp.

This tendency continues even when the infants get older. Dr. Chalmers Mitchell states: "When wild animals become tame, they are really extending or transferring to human beings the confidence and affection they naturally give to their mothers. Almost every creature that would naturally enjoy maternal care is ready to transfer its devotion to other animals or to human beings."

He goes on to point out: "The capacity to be tamed is greatest in those animals that remain longest with their parents and that are intimately associated with them."

The herbivorous (or vegetarian) animals, such as cows, rarely show any attachment toward human beings, presumably because the young don't remain long with their mothers. In contrast, the meat-eating carnivores such as the lion become very jealous of their keepers. The cow and other herbivorous animals grow into adulthood at a much faster pace than the meat-eaters. This length of time young animals spend under their mother's care is a good clue not only to their capacity for affection (apes are the most affectionate of all animals) but also to the animals' intelligence.

MOTHER LOVE

The mother camel has an overwhelming affection for her baby. She will protect and feed her offspring, and reacts to it just as a human mother does to her child.

17. Can Animals Dream—and Invent Games?

OES a fish sleep? Does a horse really sleep standing up? We assume we know the answers, but do we? Scientists have been studying the sleep of animals because they are curious to know the actual facts about animal sleep. But more important, they are looking for clues that may give them some understanding of human sleep. Science knows a lot about sleeping habits of people, but still knows pitifully little about the nature of human sleep. What actually occurs when we "fall" into sleep?

Investigators are finding that the "sleep" of some animals is more like a drowsiness than the deep sleep of Man. Cats, dogs, frogs, and guinea pigs, for example, easily succumb to drowsiness. Fish don't sleep in the same sense that mammals sleep but undergo changes in behavior toward a dormant state that bears some resemblance to sleep.

Dr. James Bender, Director of the National Institute for Human Relations, has conducted investigations into the phenomenon of sleep and has surveyed the findings of other scientists in his new book *How To Sleep*. He advises me that there are two distinct types of sleep in animals. First is the monophasic or long sleep such as most of the primates fall into. And second is polyphasic or short sleep, which is a sort of cat nap. He illustrates:

"White rats have ten rest periods around the clock, and rabbits have 16 to 21 regularly spaced naps a day."

The alligator, crocodile, and hippopotamus perform the feat of sleeping while floating on water, especially if it is warm water. They like to rest their heads on their neighbor's back.

Horses and elephants, Dr. Bender advises, actually do sleep standing up. A study that was made of 600 Army horses revealed that standing horses could fall into a deep doze, especially if they could rest their head on a manger. However, it was found that they would always lie down before falling into a really deep sleep.

Investigators watched the sleep behavior of 34 bull elephants at a circus. It was found that 29 of these elephants slept soundly (and noisily) on the ground while five elephants remained standing, in what appeared to be a doze. These five apparently were "sentries," because when two or three of them dropped down to the ground for naps, two or three others always got up, in a sort of changing of the guard. These changes occurred regularly. This practice of posting sentries is apparently a hang-over from precautions taken in the jungle.

Elephants are the loudest snorers in the animal kingdom. Once an elephant lies down, it faces quite a problem in getting up again. Some use an ant hill, if they are in the jungle, as a prop. Others roll to gather momentum.

Frequently elephants will trumpet in their sleep. This presumably means they are having bad dreams that lions or tigers are chasing them. It has been noticed, however, that there is less trumpeting if they are chained. Apparently the chain reminds them that they are in a safe place, and gives them a sense of security as they sleep. In the teak forest of India, tenderhearted mahouts often make straw chains which they tie around their elephants' ankles, to stop their nightmares.

Dr. Bender says that "most of the higher mammals give evidence of dreaming sometimes. One evidence is the way they thrash around in their 'sleep.' Most dogs emit muffled barks and growls during their sleep. Apparently some are happy dreams and some are fearful dreams."

Most creatures, of course, will seek out a soft place to sleep, but apparently of all the animals in the world only the Great Apes make a bed each night in the sense that humans make a bed. They make a frame of branches, and try to make it as soft and springy as possible. Gorillas, for example, go to a great deal of bother making a new bed each night.

The orangutan likes to make his bed up in a treetop. He selects a fork in the tree and across it lays many branches he has broken off, with the soft leafy parts toward the middle. His bed made, the orang lies out in his soft bed flat on his back, spread-eagle fashion. However, he invariably takes one precaution. Even while he sleeps he keeps the fingers of one hand locked firmly around a branch.

In cold climes where it is impractical for animals to migrate to a warmer climate—and to a climate where there may be food—Nature has invented hibernation to help many of its creatures through the coldest part of winter. Animals that hibernate have a low body temperature to start with, and go into a winter sleep when the weather drops below a certain temperature.

As an animal hibernates, curled in a ball in a snug hole, its breathing grows slower and slower, its heartbeat quiets. It has gorged itself on food for the sleep, and that food can last for weeks because all bodily activity is at a low ebb and the body has stopped growing during hibernation.

The raccoon sleeps only lightly even during the coldest part of winter and rarely goes into such a deep prolonged slumber as possesses the ground hog or chipmunk.

Almost everyone has heard of hibernation, but few people are familiar with *estivation,* the hot-weather parallel of hibernation, which a few animals experience. When water is scarce and the heat is fierce, some reptiles and amphibians, such as crocodiles and frogs, go into a dormant state resembling hibernation.

The higher we go on the evolutionary scale, according to Dr. Bender, "the more necessary sleep becomes." He states: "Every mammal with a highly developed brain requires a lot of sleep. If you keep a dog awake five straight days he will die from lack of sleep, yet he can go for a month without food. And if you force a higher mammal such as the dog to stay awake against his will he will become neurotic, and his intelligence will appear to deteriorate."

Another problem that has puzzled scientists is whether animals can really invent and play games, in the sense that humans play, for the sheer fun of it.

Certainly at first glance much that goes on looks like play. Dogs romp with each other and chase a stick you throw just for the fun of trotting back with it. . . . Squirrels dash about in the treetops chasing each other apparently just for the fun of it. . . . A young bear will lie on its back and play with its feet and toes by the hour . . . lambs frolic . . . deer jump and run . . . sea lions play tag tirelessly. Ofter they seem to be playing Follow the Leader as they climb rocks and leap into the water. I saw a frolicking sea lion scoop up a dixie cup in its mouth and spend the next ten minutes diving with it, tossing it in the air and recapturing it.

Young badgers have often been seen turning somersaults, which is quite a stunt for an animal. One investigator reports that a badger and a dog used to stage a wild free-for-all tussle every afternoon in his yard. *Furthermore, other animals almost always gathered to watch the show.*

The badger, "roaring and shaking his head like a wild boar," would charge at the dog. Often the dog would leap entirely over the lunging badger. They

THE LIFE OF RILEY

Ho-hum, another day. Albert, the South American honey bear, stretches luxuriously in the soft bed that also serves as his playground.

would chase each other wildly around the garden and frequently go into a tangle. But, he added, "there was never a real fight."

We have told of the coon that teased roosters by pulling feathers out of their tails and tossing pebbles at them. Munro Fox, the British zoologist, has reported a more advanced game played by caged chimpanzees, when chickens were near by.

If bread was placed in the cage one of the chimpanzees would sit by the bars noisily munching it (though normally chimps are not enthusiastic about bread). As he ate he would hold out a piece toward the chickens that were attracted by the sight of the bread. When the hens approached and pecked, the chimp would quickly jerk his hand back. He seemed to think this was uproariously funny.

As the game proceeded a new twist was added. Two chimps would team up to outsmart the chickens. While one held out the bread enticingly, the other would poke with a stick at any hen that came up. He adds: "The apes had obviously invented this game."

In all the animal kingdom the most playful creatures —the most enchanting and gleeful game-makers—are unquestionably the otters. Perhaps this is why some of our greatest naturalists have considered the otter as the most charming animal alive.

The otter, of course, is a member of the weasel family, with all the weasel's restless energy; but since it lives mostly in the water on a fish diet, the ferocity of the weasel has been changed to joyous exuberance in the otter.

Almost from the day baby otters are born, they begin to play; and (unlike most animals) their merrymaking continues throughout their lives. Furthermore, there is nothing sexual or seasonal about it. They play summer and winter. Two otters can spend a rollicking half-hour playing tug of war with a stick, or playing with a chip of bark that dances on the water. In the winter a favorite sport is to sprint on the ice like boys on an icy sidewalk, then throw on the brakes and skid.

Their favorite and most spectacular game is the otter slide. An otter will get up on a bank leading to the water's edge and roll down the hill into the water. Another follows, and another. Gradually the weeds are cleared, the dirt is converted into smooth, slippery mud by the wet bodies of the otters.

Now they have the slide, and otters by the dozens gather for an afternoon of great fun. Each takes his turn, goes to the top and then swooshes down toward the water, flat on his belly with his front legs folded back. Smack! He hits the water with his coat muddy. A few seconds later he comes to the surface with his coat glisteningly clean. While he waits his turn for his next slide, he wrestles and romps with other otters.

Why do the otters do this? One naturalist says, "It is done simply out of a bursting gladness."

Scientists are reluctant, however, to concede that all animal "play" is done in sport just for the fun of it, especially the play of young animals. Often the pouncing and dashing of young animals can be accounted for as either "letting off steam," or as the perfecting of instincts.

Baby skunks stage mock fights over fishheads and make believe they are very bloodthirsty. . . . Young

GET OUT OF THE RAIN

These sea lions are having the time of their lives taking a shower bath. If there is an audience, they will have twice as much fun.

foxes and coons both practice stealing up on each other undetected. . . . Young dogs snarl and gnash as they tussle. . . . Young squirrels practice edging their bodies stealthily around a tree trunk.

Are they "playing" or are they clumsily trying to perfect talents they will need to survive?

Kittens spend hours pouncing at a ball or spool. It is apparently instinctive with them to pounce on any small moving object, and Nature is training them for the day when they will pounce on mice and rats. Mother cats often move their tails slowly and watch as the kittens leap at it. Later they will bring half-killed mice for the young to pounce on. Leopards, panthers and wild cats do the same. They bring horribly maimed victims home for the young to tear at until the poor victims finally die.

Significantly, most animals as they grow older (the otters are the notable exception) do less and less "playing." Another important point is that very few animals below the mammal engage in any activity that even looks like play. There is a question whether they have the necessary brain structure to even experience pleasure.

Finally, it is probably significant that we see the most evidences of playing in animals that are fairly helpless when born, animals that take a relatively long time passing through childhood to maturity. The rodents such as the rabbits, guinea pigs and mice, develop to maturity at a very rapid rate, and it has been noticed that these animals show little tendency to "play." Perhaps it is because their instincts are nearly perfect at birth and don't need to be practiced.

The answer probably is that play in animals can be both instinct-perfection and exuberance. At any rate it is evident that play is a key to intelligence. We encounter it more and more as we come up the evolutionary scale toward Man.

18.   Animals Have Snobs and Despots, Too

HE cow—which has been called the Foster Mother of the Human Race—is a fascinating animal. Studies have shown she is so dumb she doesn't know her own name. Yet any farmer will tell you she is smart enough to get her way, can be exasperatingly stubborn, coy, placid or irritable, and adores being pampered.

Dr. W. E. Petersen, Professor of Dairy Husbandry at the University of Minnesota, has spent more than a quarter of a century trying to understand the cow. In the pasture a herd of cows appears to be just an aimless conglomeration of bovines, but Dr. Petersen has found that actually cows have a rigid and intricate social order.

Cow Society, in fact, is more snooty than New York's 400. Every single cow in the herd has her place. Toward all cows who are *above* her on the social scale, Gertrude is respectful. She will always step aside to let her social superiors drink first at the watering trough. But toward all cows who are *below,* she is a little despot.

In every herd there is a top queen. She may not be the prettiest or biggest—in fact she may have only three teats or have a lame leg—but she still runs things her way at all times. Every other cow in the herd is a humble subject.

She wins her position as dowager queen by being the toughest, buttingest cow in the herd. To be queen she had to butt it out with every cow. These butting contests can be fierce, but usually they are half butt, half bluff. The cow that backs down never again challenges the winner. Thus the cow dowager, unlike a human dowager, does not have to lose nervous energy wondering whether her subjects are plotting to unseat her.

Dr. Petersen has found that the queen of them all in a herd has many interesting prerogatives. She has first crack at the best grass in the pasture, and gets the choicest milking stall. When the herd goes walking, she leads the way. And when the herd has to go through a door or gate, the subjects all stand respectfully aside while the queen goes first. Cow No. 2 in the social order usually goes second, and so on. Last cow in the barn is the dope, who has been outbutted by every other cow.

A newcomer in the herd must butt it out with every cow to settle her position. If she outbutts the ruling queen the queen is deposed, and often takes it very badly.

Don Eddy, a magazine writer, traveled many thousand miles to have audiences with Cow Queens and ex-Cow Queens for a hilarious article, *Why Is A Cow?* He told about a famous Midwestern queen of a large herd who was sold and placed in a new herd.

"No one knows what happened during that first night, but in the morning it was evident the erstwhile queen had been whipped and didn't like it. From a complacent individual, she became first a stubborn malcontent and gradually a savage maniac.

"She had never kicked in all her well-mannered queenly life; now she exhibited a ferocious skill at kicking backward, forward and to either side. She charged her handlers, wrecked her stall, smashed a milking machine, and sent a milker to the hospital. To the end of her days—and they were numbered—she remained hopelessly insane, all because she had lost her regal place in cow society."

Another transplanted and deposed queen that Eddy

saw was a sulking neurotic and (with what might be cunning) was letting her milk down only when she felt like it. Since she had been a phenomenal milk-producer, her slow-down strike produced results. She was placed back in her original herd. "She kicked up her heels and frisked about the pasture like a calf, greeting her old subjects with playful affection," Eddy reported. "Although she had been gone a long time they instantly recognized her, and restored her queenly rank—and her milk production zoomed back to its former high level within a matter of days."

We all know office workers and factory workers who become as irritable as a cow when they believe they have been demoted to a lower rank in a strange herd of people. And in human society as a whole, outside the new world of America, we find many people who would not think of trying to rise above their assigned station in life. Many human societies have their butt order. Stuart Chase, in his *Proper Study of Mankind,* writes:

"Anthropologists have agreed that the typical human society, except in periods of very rapid change, comes to rest with nearly every individual in it enjoying a definite status. The normal individual, moreover, takes pride in his status and does not dream of revolting against it."

One of the most revealing aspects of Dr. Petersen's study of bovine psychology is the temper and mood he has found in cows at different levels on the social scale. Those near the top, just below the queen, strangely show the most frustration and neurosis and are the most unpredictable milk producers. They are most likely to be the malcontents.

Why? Dr. Petersen believes it is because these cows have won enough victories to taste the pleasures of superiority. They are ambitious, but just miss being aggressive enough in their butting to be top cow. They brood about the honors they might have snatched, and resent being pushed around by the Queen Cow.

AH, THE FRIENDLY COW...

But Bossy isn't friendly at all. In fact, she is very snooty. Each cow has her place in a herd. The queen wins hers by beating her fellows in butting contests. Ex-queens often become neurotic and refuse to give milk.

In contrast, the cows far down the social scale are accustomed to being pushed around and take it for granted. They aren't ambitious, and are content with their lot. They are the steadiest milk producers.

Scientists are finding that cows are not the only species that have rigid social orders. In fact, they are discovering that all animals that live in groups tend, under pressure of competition for the available food, to develop, in the words of one scientist, "consistent arrangements of dominance and submissiveness."

At the Bronx Zoo, Dr. Riess and his associates spent most of one summer studying the social order of a herd of Barbary sheep. There were 12 animals: four male, four female and four young. Every single one was paired up with each of the other 11 in a test to see which would grab for food that was placed before both of them.

Here again a rigid butting order, or pattern of dominance emerged. The oldest, biggest, huskiest ram was deferred to by each of the other 11. Furthermore, the scientists found a straight line dominance relationship. All four rams dominated all the ewes (female) and lambs. And four ewes dominated all the lambs, except when their own children were involved.

In a variation of the test, the scientists constructed a feed box at the end of a narrow stall so that only one sheep could eat at a time. Under this test situation the sheep followed the identical order. The biggest male always was permitted to eat first. When he had his fill, the second largest male stepped in, and so on down to the smallest lamb.

With the sheep, however, there seemed to be no relationship between "dominance" and "leadership," which apparently is a somewhat different trait. The boss ram didn't necessarily decide when they would take excursions, or lead the way when they did.

Dr. John Paul Scott found at the Jackson Memorial

Laboratory at Bar Harbor, Maine, that with ordinary goats there was a similar butt order or system of dominance. He went one step further. Dr. Scott sought to find what would happen to their social order under pressure. He began making the goats wait a few hours for their food.

This frustrating delay produced quick irritability. Fighting broke out all over the place. Dr. Scott noted with fascination, however, that a goat, no matter how irritable and hungry, never attacked his social betters. He always began picking on some goat lower down the scale. (Perhaps this situation inspired the saying: "I don't want to be the goat.") The dominant goats abused their inferiors, and those inferiors in turn took it out on goats of still lower standing.

Industrial psychologists have noticed this same phenomenon in human society. If a factory foreman has been criticized by his superiors, he will usually take the criticism unblinkingly. But later if he is unskilled in human relations he may pour out his seething anger upon his own underlings.

In chicken yards, we find a variation of the butt-order. Schjelderup-Ebbe was the first to discover that in a yard full of hens there is a rigid society based on the "peck order." The top hen has the right to walk up and peck every other hen in the entire yard without fear of retaliation. And the bottom hen leads an abject life since it has to submit to pecks, and threats of pecks, from every other hen in the yard.

According to Schjelderup-Ebbe, two hens never live in the same yard without deciding which is the despot. If two stranger hens meet, they always have it out on the spot. At the start both appear frightened, but the one that gets a grip on its fears first and is able to advance menacingly usually triumphs, without resorting to actual combat.

This first encounter is of tremendous significance. In

rare cases there may be individual revolts against a low rating in the peck order, but there is never any organized insurrection with subjects rising up to attack the queen.

Another fascinating peculiarity of the hen's social order is that a hen fairly far down the scale is apt to be more despotic with the few unhappy creatures under her, than is the top queen who has many subjects. If a low-ranking, despotic hen is transferred to another flock where she wins herself a higher place on the scale, her despotism toward those under her becomes milder.

Again this same phenomenon has been noticed in human society. A sergeant is more apt to be a bully than a major general.

A final parallel is that every new hen in a flock has to peck it out with every hen in the flock before she is accepted and given any status. The same behavior can be found in boys and girls. A new boy to the neighborhood must undergo many lickings and slug it out with practically every kid on the street before he is accepted into the gang.

Among the higher primates we likewise find that when any two chimps or monkeys meet for the first time, there is usually a struggle or bluffing match to see who's going to be boss. In primate society, however, a cunning individual can sometimes improve his lot.

In a monkey cage there are always bosses and subjects. If you put food into the cage where there are two monkeys, the boss will take charge of it all. If he catches the weaker monkey trying to sneak some food into its chum's pouch, he will often reach his hand right into the poor creature's pouch and take it out again.

In experiments at the Yerkes Laboratories of Primate Biology scientists would drop a banana down a chute to two chimps in a cage. They found that the male always monopolized the chute, except during certain phases of the female's sexual cycle, when she was permitted more food and liberties.

Henry W. Nissen of the Yerkes Laboratories has reached the following conclusions about social rank among these advanced members of the animal world:

"Sheer strength plays an important role in determining dominance and leadership, but it is by no means the only factor shaping the pattern of social relationships within a group of chimpanzees. Ingenuity, trickery, bribery and guile may become more effective than brute force. Some individuals are very successful in getting others to fight their battles or to assist them in a task requiring co-operation."

In testing two female chimps, Lia and Nira, Dr. Herbert Birch found that Lia was clearly the dominant and Nira clearly the submissive animal in the pair. He would place a test nut before them. Lia took possession of the nut so often that Nira would reach apologetically and hesitantly. When her hand was almost there, Lia would calmly reach ahead and take the nut right from under poor Nira's hand. Dr. Birch reports that in one such frustrating instance Nira's behavior was quite human:

"Nira, instead of protesting or withdrawing her hand, continued her movement, carried her hand up to her face and scratched."

When Dr. Birch had established that Nira was clearly the underdog, he injected her with shots of sex hormone. Soon he had the amazing spectacle of the once cringing Nira becoming unquestionably the dominant ape of the pair. There could be little doubt, he concluded, that the increase of Nira's sex hormone level increased her dominance drive.

Similar experiments with hens have shown that when hens low in social rank are injected with sex hormones they soon become rambunctious and aggressive, and peck their way right up to the very top of hen society.

Thus it appears that an animal's status in its particular society depends on its aggressiveness. And its aggressiveness apparently depends to a large extent upon its sex drive.

In most animal societies the males are clearly dominant over the females. A rooster, for example, normally has the "peck right" over all the hens in the yard. Male baboons are monstrous tyrants who keep their females almost constantly in cowed subjugation.

But in some animal societies it is the female that is dominant. The most conspicuous example of this in the entire animal kingdom is with deer, who have a matriarchal rather than a patriarchal society. The report of investigators at the Bronx Zoo states:

"The big Sika doe was the absolute boss of the herd under the paired feeding situation and in group feeding."

Likewise the report of another investigation to the *Journal of Comparative and Physiological Psychology* states: "Among the Red Deer in Scotland, the usual leader of the herd is an old female—and the males bring up the rear."

Despite his giant antlers and powerful build, the noble stag is actually pretty much of a mouse. Even during the mating season, when he collects a group of females for his harem, he is still not the boss. It is always a female that watches for danger, and leads the retreat.

Psychologists have noticed in studying animal behavior that most of the higher, "human" traits of animals are found more often in solitary than in herd animals. The dumbest birds, for example, are those which, like the starling, fly in large flocks; whereas the birds of prey and the highly skilled nest-builders are solitary. Likewise the dumb, cud-chewing ruminants such as the cow, sheep and bison are herd animals; whereas the cunning carnivores such as tigers and foxes are largely solitary. Zoologist Munro Fox states:

"Herding animals are of all the higher animals the most devoid of social instincts; maternal care is poorly developed, they are lacking in affection and sympathy, they are the most stupid of quadrupeds, and are in every respect greatly inferior to the solitary carnivores." The solitary creature—the lone wolf—must of necessity live more by its own wits.

The superiority of the solitary creature in Nature may offer us a helpful lesson in our own human society. Today the momentous issue that grips the world is whether Man can thrive and develop his full talents best under a herd society, such as is practiced in some areas of the world, or under an individualistic society, such as is practiced or considered as ideal in many countries, including America. The lesson of Nature favors the rugged individual.

Whatever the lesson we can learn from the highly individualistic animals, it is certainly true that Man can learn a great deal about himself by studying the behavior of his "dumb" neighbors on this planet. And he can have fun doing it.

*In addition to the photographs by Lilo Hess
from Three Lions, Inc., acknowledgment is
made to Yale Laboratories of Comparative Psychobiology for the photograph on page 139.*

THE NEW
Rand McNally
POCKET
WORLD
ATLAS

■ The most complete pocket atlas ever published

■ Legible, detailed maps of every state, country and continent, including 72 pages in full color

■ Latest official census figures

■ Thousands of up-to-date geographic facts and figures

■ Complete Gazetteer Index of World